DISCARDED
JENKS LRC
GORDON COLLEGE

NEWTONIAN SCIENCE

By the same author

CHRISTIAN HUYGENS AND THE RISE OF SCIENCE IN THE SEVENTEENTH CENTURY

NEWTONIAN SCIENCE

ARTHUR E. BELL

LONDON
EDWARD ARNOLD (PUBLISHERS) LTD.

First published 1961

For

LAURENCE

and

HARRIET

Printed in Great Britain
by W. & J. Mackay & Co Ltd, Chatham

PREFACE

A great work of art gives us more than pleasure. It enhances and enlarges our whole experience. This is true of the greatest achievements in scientific thought. For they bring a profound significance to ordinary events and add a dimension to our thinking about the world.

It would be tragic if we had to choose between the artistic and literary part of our culture on the one hand, and the mathematical and scientific part on the other. There is an absurdity in the very suggestion. But modern life presses us in this direction and we feel, perhaps rather vaguely, that science needs to be seen in a wider context.

This essay is an attempt to do this. It is an attempt, also, to bring out some of the points of strength and of weakness that can be seen when we look back on the science of the past.

My sincere thanks are due to my friend and former colleague Mr. Godfrey Hainton for reading the proofs and advising me over a number of corrections and alterations.

ARTHUR E. BELL

Cheltenham, 1960

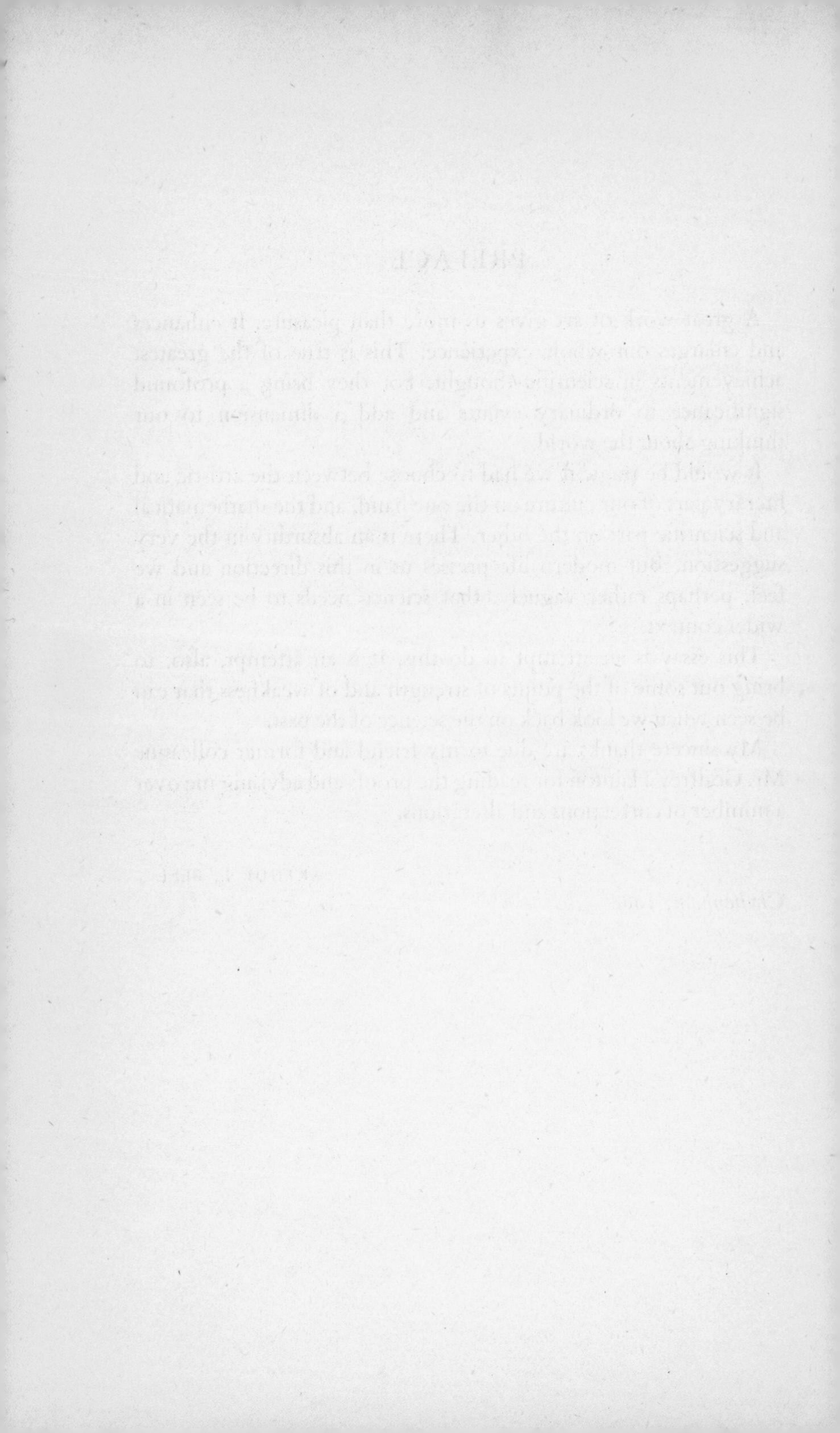

CONTENTS

'For, indeed, a change was coming upon the world, the meaning and direction of which even still is hidden from us, a change from era to era . . . all the forms, desires, beliefs, convictions of the old world were passing away never to return. A new continent had risen up beyond the western sea. The floor of heaven, inlaid with stars, had sunk back into an infinite abyss of immeasurable space; and the firm earth itself, unfixed from its foundations, was seen to be but a small atom in the awful vastness of the universe. In the fabric of habit which they had so laboriously built for themselves, mankind were to remain no longer.'

J. A. FROUDE

INTRODUCTION

THIS book is a treatment, all on its own, of one particular chapter in the history of science. The scene today is totally changed and it is difficult to recapture in imagination the circumstances, the events, and the personalities that made the seventeenth century the age it was. For it was an age quite unlike our own in very many respects. It was an age that produced in France Louis XIV, Colbert, Descartes and Pascal, and in England, Cromwell, Hobbes, Milton, Locke, the Royal Society and Isaac Newton. In music there was Purcell; in painting the wonderful Spanish and Flemish schools; in the theatre, Racine and Molière. Since it was such a critical age in science it would be useful to have an account of all the work that was going on. Yet such an account might seriously lack the element of drama that pertains to a wider view. It could easily appear dull to a modern reader. To describe in broad outline how the great synthesis achieved by Isaac Newton came about is a more untidy but a much more exciting task and it is hoped that some of this excitement can be caught from the pages that follow.

To write about 'Newtonian Science' is to attempt a considerable degree of simplification. Up to the writing of Newton's *Principia* (published in 1687) no one could know that this great clarification of ideas and summing up of physical science would come about—not even Newton knew, it appears, until he began his work just how far it could be carried through. It was not until the end of the eighteenth century that the idea of *energy* was introduced into science. But we can see that the conceptions employed towards the end of the seventeenth century guaranteed the success of the whole scientific venture. This is the best defence that can be offered for the title of this essay. For it might be hotly debated whether there was such a thing as 'Newtonian Science', seeing how much Newton was indebted to Kepler, Galileo and others and considering how much exacting experimental work had to be done to extend the boundaries of science even into the more elementary parts of physics and chemistry. The *Principia* was a very great book but it takes us hardly anywhere in the history of physics. What it did was to show what physics might be. Perhaps it would be better to say that it showed what science might be. Yet a discussion of how the *Principia* came to be written, what was in it, and what were the subsequent effects of the work, does not turn out to be a specially technical matter.

This essay has been written, not for scientists, but for all who care about science as a precious part of our European heritage. It has been written just because we have had such barbarous perversions of science in modern times and because it would be a tragedy if we no longer saw science as a great intellectual venture but came to think of it as nothing but a set of useful techniques. To think of science as technique is becoming more and more the tendency of modern times. Applied science and technology are paramount in our thinking about the future. We are, it is said, in the midst of a second industrial revolution, which means the application of theoretical knowledge, no longer in the half-hearted manner of the past, but full-blast and all-out. In the leisurely decades of the last century there were many discoveries which could have been instantly pursued and turned to practical account. This did not happen because the ruling class in England was not educated to see the possibilities, through industry, of scientific techniques. The interest of science was then predominantly intellectual, and even so its pursuit was half-hearted.

Our present age is a period of great stress because the intellectual achievements of science amount to a new view of the world, while the pursuit of science as technique may well hand our civilization over to a new form of barbarism. We need to preserve the sense of science as intellectual achievement and not lose sight of those relations which link it with an older form of culture. So that we keep our awareness of an essential continuity in our civilization. Without this science can easily become a disruptive force.

That scientific research will transform men's ideas seems inescapable. We have to be ready to follow the light wherever it leads, and we do not know how much, in another hundred years, will seem archaic and ignorant in our present ways of thinking. It is much more important that we should see that science will transform life than that it will revolutionize industry. Since wealth can be gained in the second of these pursuits this is the one that is attracting all our attention. Yet it is the first that is really more important, and the pages of this essay provide a brief survey of how, in an early part of the scientific movement, the two pursuits began. For science, while it is a transforming force in civilization, has its roots far back in our Graeco-Roman past, and its accelerated development in the seventeenth century did not at first result in that dualism in our culture which many feel to exist, and fear, in modern times. Essentially this may have been because science was not excluded from a philosophy which took account of other things. Only later, as A. N. Whitehead and Bertrand Russell have shown, has this influence of science in our civilization become gradually dominant, so that other points of view that may lack a scientific kind of validity have been put on the defensive, or have been simply ignored and forgotten. The realization of the nature of science came home to a particular group of men in the seventeenth century and affected them in a peculiarly forceful manner. At that time no alternative view of science as technique was really possible, or at all likely to become a dominant point of view. But there seems to be no doubt of the forcefulness of the realization that there was in science a new form of inquiry and a new type of systematic knowledge. Science did not arise all at once or even very suddenly and it would be going too far to say that it has created the modern world. But ever since the seventeenth century it has been a powerful intellectual force; certainly, one would say, the greatest single co-operative enterprise not only in modern times, but in the whole history of the human race. It is understandable that many should feel reluctant to set limits to the results of this enterprise now that its existence has become recognized at long last, and now that it is proceeding to dominate our views of education.

The seventeenth century recognized that scientific law was the essence of the new knowledge. The issue was clouded quite as much as it was clarified, by the various writers of that period just because the new studies could not be easily assessed and because their significance appeared uncertain. Galileo wrote quite wittily about science and, like Francis Bacon and Descartes, he saw it in opposition to the accepted authorities to whom men had previously turned. Nevertheless it took time to realize what was peculiar about the subjects that were established about this time. In this little book the extensive literature on plants and animals, and all the 'curious' information that was collected together in that period of enthusiasm, have been completely ignored. So, too, has the literature of alchemy and astrology, neither of which bore any intellectual fruit worth mentioning. Instead attention has been almost completely confined to the subjects of astronomy and mechanics because those were the subjects which brought out the essential qualities which were in future to be required of all the most progressive branches of science.

For the characteristic of science that is both most striking and most fertile in results is the characteristic of natural law expressed in mathematical form. This means that in some way or other inquiry can lead us to discover, or some would prefer to say formulate, a law that applies to a whole range of phenomena. That the law can be expressed in mathematical form is of still greater importance because this means that really significant concepts have been arrived at, and that the relation between these concepts is of a relatively simple form.

We have no justification, it appears, *a priori,* for assuming that natural laws are of such simplicity that we can arrive at a valid formulation of them. But such a faith is essential in science, and on the whole, with various reservations, the faith seems to be justified. Nor need we become sidetracked into a lengthy and inconclusive argument whether the laws apply objectively, or are instead résumés of our 'experience'. There are many such philosophical problems that attracted attention in the nineteenth century and it may be that too many complications have tended to obscure the original conception. For the original conception, that is best illustrated in Newton's *Philosophiae Naturalis Principia Mathematica,* is the conception of science that rests on the discovery of natural law and its fullest exploitation in the explanation of phenomena that are related together.

The realization that the fundamental regularities of nature are of this sort was the essential advance that makes the seventeenth century the turning-point in the history of science. Much that belongs chronologically to the period can be totally ignored if we are trying to seize this essential fact. Imaginatively the idea is indeed splendid. We need only one or two examples and it is not hard to imagine that in the whole realm of nature there are mathematical regularities, which cannot be superseded, but which, one on top of another, give rise to all the resultant complexities that are seen to exist. How this point of view was encouraged can be seen in the further investigations of eighteenth-century astronomers who sought to complete the many details that were lacking in Newton's original treatment. Throughout the whole physical realm, then, it follows that we should be able in time to discover laws of the most far-reaching sort, according to which changes take place. So that given a suitable formulation of the general laws particular examples of their action can readily be deduced. This is as near as a brief statement can perhaps come to an explanation of the nature of scientific law. The following pages will, it is hoped, do more to clarify the problem, and show how men were influenced by the new kind of knowledge that is represented by science, especially by that unified development within a single framework of ideas, that we call Newtonian science.

Newtonian science was the great culminating achievement of the late seventeenth century and the eighteenth century. It is very surprising that scientists like Kelvin tried to preserve the system well into the nineteenth century when, it is clear to us now, the new subjects of electro-magnetic induction and electro-magnetism demanded fresh conceptions. Today Newtonian science is a museum piece, and the extent to which it continues to dominate all early science teaching is almost anachronistic. But there can be no doubt that we ought to study the way in which it arose, and this broadly speaking is the aim of this little book.

It would be very instructive to try and present this part of the history of science against a detailed background of social and economic history. In a short account, however, it would be easy to lose the thread which in this case is the pursuit of certain intellectual ideas. All that will be attempted, therefore, can appropriately be included in this *Introduction*, after which we need refer only to certain critics or opponents of science who spoke from some special point of view: men like Pope or Swift or Berkeley who had their own reasons for criticizing the new movement.

The reasons for their opposition to science need examining. For the majority of men interested themselves in all manner of problems that no longer mattered, and they did not see that the new problems raised in scientific inquiry were the most important of their age. An intense parochialism seems to be the lot of most men in any age. Often, when changes occur slowly, this may not matter very much. But the parochialism of the seventeenth century was inauspicious. It may well have come from the limited opportunities for education, and still more from the lack of information about contemporary affairs that today is supplied by press and radio. This information about the changes going on was lacking, and so, not only in the seventeenth century, but up to modern times, few men have lived with anything but fragmentary information about the major circumstances governing their lives. A brief historical survey will help to bring out how serious were the changes that occurred in the seventeenth century. For the intellectual revolution was a product, in some form, of great changes in the world of human affairs. Invasions and wars even played their part in the production of Newton's *Principia*. Certainly, before we consider the intellectual advances in the scientific field it seems necessary to recall briefly what kind of world it was in which these took place.

It is very interesting to note that several writers of the sixteenth and seventeenth centuries believed themselves to be living in an age of discovery and expansion. There were, of course, voyages, from the middle of the sixteenth century, to find a north-easterly, or a north-westerly passage to the east which must have fostered this belief. For these were only the successors to the earlier and more successful achievements of the Portuguese sailors who had opened up the Cape route to India. But why had these events come about just when they did? When did a world which had long seen the Mediterranean lands as the centre of civilization give place to one where navigation across the oceans to India and China, to America, and around the globe was taken for granted? H. A. L. Fisher, in his *History of Europe*, gives traditional prominence to the penetration of Western Europe by the Turks and to the fall of Constantinople, the capital of the Eastern Roman Empire, in 1453. This meant that important trade routes were denied to European countries after they had been kept open for two thousand years. There was, as is well known, no power or combination of powers in Europe at that time capable of expelling the Turks. This meant much more than a loss of trade and wealth for, as H. A. L. Fisher remarks, the Turk did not value the culture of the West and remained an alien in the land he conquered. Frederick III, the last Emperor of the West to be crowned in Rome, was in a key position to organize resistance to the Turks, but he failed to take any decisive action. He was, says Fisher, 'as great a nullity as ever played an important part in History'. In the Italian city states which represented at that time the peak of achievement in western civilization the situation was hopeless because they were constantly engaged in their own quarrels. Writing of Milan, Venice and Florence, Fisher remarks: 'The precious and irredeemable years during which it would have been possible, had there been a concerted Italian effort, to save Europe from the Turks, were consumed by three of the wealthiest and most advanced communities in the world in a contest which had no significance for civilization.'

It does not do, however, to suppose that the Turkish invasion was the sole cause of the great changes that were taking place. Indeed some writers now speak as if the invasion were of relatively small importance compared with other circumstances they are at pains to emphasize. Thus, the northern states had long been jealous of the monopoly of trading in the Mediterranean that was enjoyed by the Italians, and the profits made by middlemen who handled the over-land trade through Egypt were perhaps resented just as much. Certainly the history of oceanic voyages by Europeans takes us back much earlier than the events of 1453. Marco Polo's exploits belong to the thirteenth century, for example, and the voyages of Portuguese sailors further and further south along the coast of Africa belong to the early decades of the fifteenth century. Indeed, after the Portuguese opened up their route to the East *via* the Cape they did not want the Mediterranean routes to flourish. How far some of the early voyages were prompted by the desire of discovery, how far they were attempts to find new trade routes, and how far they were, occasionally, involuntary will remain an interesting matter of speculation. It is clear that commercial enterprise and national rivalry prompted many of them. Nor were the failures always less important than the successes. In such severe conditions as were encountered by the Dutch and English sailors in the Arctic regions it must have been realized that better geographical information, better methods of navigation, and better ships were needed. The failure of these northerly voyages in fact compelled the English and Dutch to enter into direct competition with the Portuguese in the Indian Ocean and this they did successfully through possessing superior ships, superior technical knowledge and better finances. Yet on the whole English attempts came late. It was not until 1577–80 that an English sailor circumnavigated the globe. The experience of 1588 was of course very important yet it was not for a very long time that an empire founded on sea power appeared a remote possibility.

It seems to have been in the early seventeenth century that a few minds became intensely aware that great changes were taking place in the world. Francis Bacon, for example, was very aware, and made his countrymen aware, of important intellectual changes that were taking place or by that time had taken place. It was a happy choice of his to make the frontispiece of his *Novum Organum* a picture of a ship in full sail making her way into the Atlantic Ocean between the Pillars of Hercules—here represented as stone pillars, symbolizing the limits of the old intellectual world. 'It would indeed be dishonourable to mankind,' he wrote, 'if the regions of the material globe, the Earth, the Sea, and Stars should be so prodigiously developed and illustrated in our age, and yet the boundaries of the Intellectual globe should be confined to the narrow discoveries of the ancients.' We must see Bacon's writings on philosophy as in important respects a statement by a man of the late Renaissance, not a man of science of the seventeenth century. But the importance of Bacon was that he was extremely readable. In the midst of a life of public affairs he caught up and emphasized the idea of intellectual exploration just as his countrymen were becoming aware of the importance of geographical exploration.

For, after the preparations of the fifteenth century, the sixteenth and seventeenth centuries saw sea-faring Europeans visiting almost every part of the world. To do this they had to reject as superstitious the ancient fears of the great oceans and the belief of Arab sailors that they were unnavigable. A little reflection will show, however, how this belief arose. The 'portolan' charts of the time were restricted to the known coast lines; they were not in our sense of the term maps, because they were not based on a consistent projection of the earth's surface. They were criss-crossed with lines giving compass bearings of natural features. Having regard to such limitations it is surprising that navigation was as good as it often was. The astrolabe was the standard instrument for taking observations of the stars but its use at sea was fraught with difficulties. A much simpler form than that now commonly seen in museums (such as the Ashmolean Museum at Oxford) was used by mariners, but then, as a rule, it was used on landing in some foreign place. The compass was a far more important aid in navigation. On his second voyage to the New World Columbus is said to have left his astrolabe at home. Much the worst handicap was the impossibility of determining longitude. Had this been possible Columbus would certainly have doubted if Cuba could be part of the mainland of Asia. The determination of longitude remained an unsolved problem up to the end of the seventeenth century. Thus, out of sight of land, sailing on a compass, and at night with the aid of the stars, the early navigators of the Atlantic and Pacific oceans needed to be men of great courage and tenacity.

The Europeans, however, once they began these voyages, showed their superiority over Arab sailors through their ability to turn technical knowledge to practical use. Exploration, commerce, and military power resulting from the development of fire-arms were certainly among the early incentives to the study of science, although in all these the practical men went ahead of scientific study and made their advances in more empirical ways. The design of ships and of the sails they carried changed quite considerably. Square rig sails are excellent for going before the wind, but with square rig alone a fleet can be kept in harbour by an adverse wind. The lateen sail used by the Arabs was early adopted by Portuguese sailors and from them it spread to other nations, so that combinations of lateen type sails and square rig sails became common. With the development of cannon the fighting power of a ship no longer depended on its crossbow and arquebus fire from the raised fo'c'sle and poop but on the ability to fire a broadside, the cannon being mounted between decks. The first mathematical study of the trajectory of a bullet was that by the Italian, Tartaglia (1537). The Dutch engineer Simon Stevin is a most interesting example of the type of man the seventeenth century was to produce. An excellent engineer, he was responsible for some important studies in mechanics; and he gave the first scientific record of tides without, however, attempting to explain how they arise. The great Galileo amply illustrates the way in which practical problems called for fundamental studies; part of his treatise of 1632 was devoted to the study of the mechanical strength of materials. All over Europe men began to try experiments which would lead to an understanding of such confusing things as fluid pressures and the impact of a moving body on a stationary one. Other experiments quite obviously were suggested by practical experience. Detailed studies of some of these problems, with an account of the method used in solving them, form a later part of this book. It is interesting to see that while men of many different nations began to co-operate quite closely in these theoretical studies the great developments in the world at large took place in an atmosphere of suspicion, jealousy and hostility.

Exploration, and the development of new lands, did not appeal to any Europeans in this so-called age of discovery as matters requiring co-operation and mutual assistance. The scale of the new undertakings was not at first appreciated. Quite clearly no one at that time realized how much capital was needed if new resources were to be developed; on the contrary it was commonly expected that there should be nothing but profits, without any great expenditure, from such enterprises. Then, too, European history was dominated by age-old quarrels, suspicions, and jealousies, which were perpetuated because to a large degree they were family quarrels, suspicions and jealousies. The results of the Reformation produced an additional issue and papal Bulls were published which were designed to secure that the new countries inherited the true faith, or at least were controlled by its exemplars. The discovery of rich veins of silver ore in Mexico and what is now Bolivia about the middle of the sixteenth century tended to dispel doubts about the amount of wealth to be found in the New World. Piracy was encouraged to the extent that a state of undeclared war existed between the maritime nations. The final adherence of England to Protestantism after 1559 made papal Bulls of no effect, while the defeat of the Armada in 1588 left her free to colonize. Down to this time not a single Englishman was living under the English flag in any English land beyond the sea. Less than twenty years after 1588 systematic colonization on a considerable scale had begun. Such was the new importance of sea power.

We have to admit that the failure of European nations to co-operate in matters which offered immense mutual advantages was no worse than the failures of our own time. The profound provincialism of their politics was matched by a profound provincialism of intellect generally, and that too remains unchanged. The quarrels of princes, of rival dynasties, of religious faiths, of economic powers, remain indeed relatively credible and understandable things beside the really grandiose failure of the educated half of the world to perceive its common lot as occupiers of a very small, very limited planet. Science in the seventeenth century was only a beginning but it was seen by a handful of men to be charged with high significance. It excited Descartes in a way quite different from the way in which it affected Locke. Huygens and Newton were at slightly different times its leading exponents but they were neither of them philosophers in the modern sense of the word. Only Voltaire, perhaps, coming later, perceived the tragi-comedy, and his wit saw the situation as one for ridicule rather than instruction.

For unhappily the greatest period for the emergence of science from its medieval background of thought was also the period when the modern states emerged as competing powers. The idea of the philosopher-king had never impressed itself upon these northern states of Europe. On the contrary the affairs of Europe were decided more by the creators of armies and the instigators of age-long quarrels, many of which took, in course of time, such unforeseen courses, that causes and effects seem in the end to become totally unrelated and often quite incommensurable.

Germany was ruined through the Thirty Years War; England after the war of the Spanish Succession became a leading power in the world. Only France in the seventeenth century seemed to be taking the course marked out for her by the calculations of Richelieu and the ambitions of Louis XIV; and the discovery that these foundations were insecure was not made until the following century.

There were extenuating circumstances that make the seventeenth century seem, after all, quite an enlightened age despite the cruelties of its punishments and executions and the rough life which was all that was offered to the majority of mankind. It is something of a surprise to learn how in the midst of wars enemy aliens could, and did, travel to each other's countries. War was then by no means total war. And though punitive expeditions could be sharp and ruthless the military forces of the time lacked the means to launch any but quite small armies or maintain them long in engagements. The result was that battles were soon over, both on land and at sea, and for whole seasons of the year aggression need not be feared. Compared with medieval times the areas in which life could be lived securely and pleasantly in the newer type of manor house greatly increased. Fortified castles fell into disuse, communications improved, and town building began to sprawl at ease beyond the old city walls. The rise of a new merchant class, together with an improvement in the status of the lawyer and the physician, gave an impetus to education which was no longer tied to the needs of the Church. 'A society divided between lay and cleric gave place to a society divided into rich and poor, an atmosphere hostile to free enquiry to one in which science could live and mature.' (H. A. L. Fisher, *History of Europe*, p. 431.)

A great deal of the change that took place in the seventeenth century can be seen to be the result of a mobilization of intelligence and ability from a much larger class than in the past. It seems to be no accident that in England the mid-seventeenth century saw the rise both of science and of parliamentary power. Rule by the old aristocracy was superseded. The new men who came to the fore were to a large extent free from the prepossessions which had so often hindered new enterprises. Having less private wealth they saw the need of organization and began to think of prosperity as a function of national income. It is significant that the Dutch were always solvent during the seventeenth century whereas aristocratic Spain despite her overseas empire existed in a chronic state of insolvency. Even monarchs, however, began to realize that wealth could be earned and that without it their power of action was mysteriously limited.

Colbert, the great minister first of Mazarin and then of Louis XIV, illustrates the new outlook. Not only was he responsible for many reforms in French internal affairs, he was extremely active in colonization, in the establishing of two great French trading companies, in the building of a French fleet, and in the establishing of learned societies. Far better than Bacon he saw the importance of science and how scientists should be enabled to do their work. Less visionary, more practical, he belongs to the seventeenth century as Bacon does not. But it was characteristic of the age that he died profoundly disappointed, unable to curb or control the actions of stupid and powerful men. Monarchs began to see, however, that wealth was needed if an efficient army was to be maintained. 'The crucial point was finance. Not only the change in size, but all the other great changes in armies during this period were made possible because the states became richer. They developed an efficient taxing system, and this was made possible both by economic changes, by deliberate political effort and invention, and by the pressure of military necessities. Just as the modern state was needed to create the standing army, so the army created the modern state, for the influence of the two causes was reciprocal.' (Sir George Clark, *The Seventeenth Century*, p. 101.)

Thus there was a good deal more organization and administration in the seventeenth century state than there had been in former times, a characteristic of our civilization which has now reached over-large proportions. The word complex cannot perhaps be used of European civilization until the nineteenth century, but the origins of its complexity can be discerned two centuries earlier in the founding of large-scale enterprises, whether these were military, economic, or governmental. The founding of so many grammar schools and colleges in England in the sixteenth and seventeenth centuries is a sure index of the change we are discussing.

Printing, of course, played a very great part in this quickening of the tempo of life. From the time of the Aldine Press at Venice printing had served to spread the works of Greek and Roman authors, of the humanists, of the Reformers, and now of the mathematicians and scientists all over Europe. It was this, indeed, that gave to the states of Europe which are so very diverse in their traditions the one essential for a common civilization.

Certainly the seventeenth century brought about an interest in intellectual achievement that was quite a new thing in the history of English thought. H. A. L. Fisher goes so far as to say that it was science that gave England a place in the intellectual life of Europe, a place which the insular reputation of a Shakespeare or a Milton could not have secured. 'For at the death of Queen Elizabeth and right down to the days of Oliver Cromwell England counted for little in Europe.' (*History of Europe,* p. 642.) It would be encouraging to think that the intellectual distinction of a Huygens or a Newton could win admiration abroad for the countries that produced them; encouraging but untrue in the broad sense. For one thing it was only a tiny minority that could understand mathematical work, and the most important work of the seventeenth century was mathematical. For another, scientific inquiries had in some sense to be established as important in practice and significant for thought—and on both counts there remained as much scepticism as conviction by the end of the century. As R. G. Collingwood remarked in his *Autobiography* the importance of the new inquiries was enough to divide the thinkers of the period into those who saw their importance and those who did not. 'The first group comprised all those whose names are now generally known to students of philosophy. The second, an immensely greater host of good men, learned men, subtle men, sleep their long night unknown and unlamented. . . .' For the great mass of mankind, then as now, important discoveries could only be understood when translated by action into the terms of visible change. It was not until the late eighteenth century that science began to prove its importance on account of the material benefits to which it gave rise, and not until the nineteenth century that this process could no longer be ignored. To this extent several discoveries or innovations of the seventeenth century remained little appreciated until much later. There are many parallels to be drawn here. For example the English parliamentary system, established on sound foundations, although by no means democratic foundations, must have seemed a liability and not an asset to many foreign observers. It is probably from the victories of Marlborough at Blenheim and Ramillies that we must date the admiration of foreigners for our institutions.

Thus the history of science in the seventeenth century can be seen not only as an aspect of the origins of our modern world, as something almost incidental in the affairs of states, but also as a part of the history of western civilization in all that is most characteristic in it. The opening words of Fisher's *History of Europe* are well known: 'We Europeans are the children of Hellas.' It has been the Greek influence that has worked its way out in the rise of science. As we shall see, one very interesting point that emerges from the history of scientific thought has been the evidence it gives of an essential continuity of western science with Greek thought. It is unfortunate that these developments went on, and had to go on, not in the calm atmosphere of the laboratory but against a constant background of largely irrational activity. Nor can we feel confident that the situation has changed for the better. For all the limitations of the seventeenth century, the governing powers did not hit on the idea of classifying work as secret. If the scientist was too long neglected this had its advantages. It has been the twentieth century, that age of science, that has seen scientists reduced to the position of paid hirelings of huge undertakings. Then, if we must look for antagonism to science we find it in the belief that it is from the Church and from religion that men ought to derive all they need to know. None the less there was never complete antagonism between the Christian religion and secular learning, though limited antagonisms arose quite frequently. To-day there is undoubtedly an antagonism, and it is to be found in the totalitarianism of East or West that is associated with the power of the national state. The witty Fontenelle saw all this clearly so long ago as the early eighteenth century. Kings and rulers, he said, see the earth as a fine place for the foundation of empires by military conquest. Philosophers see it as a great ball rolling through the heavens, covered with fools.

It is a relief to turn to the artistic work of the age we are studying to see what artists and craftsmen could achieve without any help from what are today regarded as scientific techniques. In the Victoria and Albert Museum in London, for example, one may see fine specimens of Venetian wrought iron from the sixteenth century, some fine silver work by the great Dutch artists, Limoges enamels of the late sixteenth century, all of which are witness to the high standard of such work at its best. For the technical resources of the seventeenth century were by no means negligible. And during the century the influences of mathematics and science began to be felt so that developments can be seen, for example, in architecture. The building of St. Paul's Cathedral between 1675 and 1710 is a memorial to the scientific spirit as well as a memorial to its great architect Sir Christopher Wren. Wren was a professor of astronomy, and a competent mathematician. Only later in life was he concerned with architecture. There are many men in this interesting period who showed astonishing virtuosity. We do not find when we study the seventeenth century that there were specialist groups at work in clearly marked off fields. Rather the contrary. The mathematicians we read about are found also at the meetings of experimentalists; they join in philosophical discussions; they are found again planning the rebuilding of London. Newtonian science owes much, indeed, to a host of men whose names are largely forgotten. The experimentalists of the first half of the century were so overshadowed by Newton that we forget their strenuous efforts to find answers to the problems that are all solved in the *Principia*.

If Newtonian science is today dead, in the sense that we no longer attempt to confine our explanations within the particular limits of Newton's scheme, nevertheless it has shaped the modern world: built its ships and engines, designed its most advanced buildings, even launched its aeroplanes, and given rise to the grandest schemes of its civil engineers. No longer philosophically important the Newtonian scheme is still of immense practical significance. For not yet has any newer scheme had the chance of imposing its pattern on the course of events. Up to the present our world has been governed by Newtonian science; the machinery, the weapons, the forces have all been such as Newtonian science can comprehend. And the emergence of this sort of study to a position of enormous importance has belatedly shocked a world which formerly supposed that mathematical symbols formed no part of a gentleman's education.

This then is our subject: the development of astronomy and mechanics, and later of physics, in accordance with a quantitative mathematical method, and their culmination in a scheme of ideas which seemed for long to possess a unique quality of truth. We know today that the Newtonian treatment is by no means the only one that is valid and we are in the midst of developments towards which Newtonian science provides hardly the slightest assistance. From this vantage-point in time let us look back on the past.

CHAPTER ONE

The Example of Johann Kepler

THE medieval view of the world made sense. In Europe this view was essentially religious and Christian. Theology was the 'queen of the sciences' and right up to Newton's time it seemed to many to be the highest exercise of the human spirit. However debased this Christian view might at times become it unquestionably gave an acceptable setting for human life. The Middle Ages was not an age of faith so much as 'an age of acquiescence'—G. G. Coulton's phrase—and we must not exaggerate the uniformity of outlook that existed amongst thinkers even within the Church. But while human beings had to endure hardship, accepting that place in society to which apparently they had been called, while there might be wars, famines, pestilences, men were not over-troubled by the desire for what we should consider to be scientific explanations. Today we take for granted, and it is an important article of a liberal faith, that all things are the better for a study which uncovers causes and effects. Yet this is a strikingly modern point of view, and even today most people are unable to detach themselves sufficiently to see the events of their lives as they see other more distant facts. In Voltaire's *Candide* the philosopher Dr Pangloss is ridiculed because he is at all times ready to expound causes and effects in human life by referring to a German philosophy that Voltaire found absurd. This was the philosophy of Leibnitz which Voltaire only imperfectly understood. It was enough for him that Leibnitz appeared to think that God had made the 'best of all possible worlds', that creation might have taken other forms, but this one we experience is the best possible. If one could believe that, Voltaire seems to say, one could believe anything. He was completely intolerant of such explanations why things are as they are. They belonged, as he saw, to a remote age. For Voltaire, writing in the eighteenth century, was heir to Newtonian science. For him the true explanations of things, if they can be obtained at all, must be essentially scientific explanations. By this time a great change had occurred in the very meaning we give to the word explanation.

For the only explanations men had in a pre-scientific age referred to reasons, which were moral reasons, why things are as they are. In the last resort these moral reasons pointed to God's purposes, or in Greek thought to purposes inherent in the nature of the universe. All such explanations which rest on some conception of the end to which things move may be called teleological (*telos,* an end), and right down to the seventeenth century such explanations easily outweighed other considerations, such as what forces might be acting on a body to cause it to move in a particular way. The great intellectual revolution of the seventeenth century lay in the realization that in the subject of mechanics it is possible to work out a system of explanations that is not teleological but thoroughly deterministic, which refers not vaguely to God's purposes or preferences but brings out the quantitative relationships that a mathematical account of phenomena requires. Not at first was the new point of view considered to be in any way atheistical nor did it appear necessarily to mean the end of a teleological philosophy of nature. Newton, for example, believed that God was the author of nature, and many of the men of science of that time considered that in the new discoveries of their time they were 'thinking God's thoughts after him'.

Today we can realize appropriately the immensity of the revolution that was accomplished in the seventeenth century even though it is not idle to speak of a 'Copernican revolution' in the century before, and even though the more we study the history of science the more we are led back to the Greeks or to the Arabs, or to scholastic thinkers who otherwise belong to a tradition that science later destroyed. For it is a travesty of the facts to think that in the rise of science one group of men, enlightened and experimental in outlook, had to contend with another group, authoritarian and repressive. Nor was the science of the seventeenth century the result simply of a reawakened interest in Greek inquiries. To give a satisfactory account several factors have to be considered in relation to each other; several distinct traditions become intertwined. Certainly in the seventeenth century itself there was no complete separation of science and philosophy such as we have today. But the result was definite and decisive. The medieval view of the world was geo-centric and concerned to moralize and show how God had man's needs in mind when he created the world. Thomas Aquinas speaks of man in this sense as the 'beneficiary of divine goodness'. The new astronomy which, after Copernicus, Galileo made irresistible was helio-centric, and the philosophy appropriate to the new scale of ideas, and the deterministic explanations of mechanics, abolished human needs as in any way relevant to the explanations accepted by educated men. Not only mechanics and physics, but all branches of learning were in time affected by the new notion of what constitutes an 'explanation'. The Black Death of the fourteenth century was generally attributed to the wickedness of mankind which had at length aroused the wrath of God. In the seventeenth century there came another visitation, but by that time intelligent opinion was quite different. Although the cause of plague was not understood, sensible measures were adopted and there was greater readiness to see the epidemic as a phenomenon which would in time be rendered explicable.

It is surprising to see how nearly, at various times, great thinkers have come to the discovery of the method of work and the mental outlook that are essential for science—and how greatly out of proportion have been the results of apparently small but in reality very significant contributions. Archimedes seems, among the Greeks, to be easily the most scientific in his methods and interests—yet he did not really succeed in reaching any important laws of mechanics and even his famous discovery in hydrostatics was not properly explained by him. The use of Hindu numerals by certain Arabic writers seems haphazard and almost accidental. The study of the more obvious problems of optics might well seem trivial. The endless arguments occasioned among the educated men of Christendom by the infiltration of new and heretical doctrines derived ultimately from Aristotle seem to belong, surely, to the history of theology rather than science. Yet it can be shown that all these things, and many others, played their part in the rise of science. For out of a number of traditions a new tradition was eventually created.

At first Christian philosophy owed much to the teaching of

Plato. Plato is easily the most poetic and spiritual, if not the greatest, of the Socratic school of philosophers. From the time of Augustine the platonist tradition in Christian thought has remained very strong. It has often been remarked, in one phrase or another, that Christianity is a religion 'in search of a philosophy', and in Plato's dialogues there was to be found a view of the relation of body and spirit, and a description of 'reality' which brought into account the absolute values of truth, beauty and goodness. It all constitutes a philosophy which seems to us today as if it was predestined to serve this end. Plato's philosophy was totally unsuited to provide even a helpful beginning in asking those questions that lead, one way or another, to the practical inquiries of physical science. Its effect was in the contrary direction because it encouraged the belief that a sufficient refinement of intellect and soul would enable men to apprehend the truth about things so far as they would ever apprehend it. It is well known that Plato contrasted *knowledge* which is spiritual and intellectual with *opinion* which might result from mere observation. He contrasted the real world of 'being' with the matter-of-fact world of 'becoming'. Observation, he taught, can teach us little and we must beware of trusting the evidence of our senses. Truth is not to be found in the world we experience since this world is so very imperfect. The real world is a world of ideal 'Forms', which are, as it were, the archetypes of ordinary things. These 'Forms' (or as they have also been called, 'Ideas') are related to the objects of sense somewhat as the conceptual triangle or circle of the mathematician is related with any actual triangle or circle he may draw on paper. We are accustomed to the notion that such figures cannot be represented in perfect accordance with our conception of them, but this is not the chief point of Plato's teaching. For him the ideal Form is not only perfect, it is also universal, in that it stands for, or embraces, all ordinary examples with all their infinite variations in detail. In addition to this the ideal Form is not merely intellectual or conceptual: it exists in the realm of the ideal which stands behind, and gives significance to, the world of sense.

More than this can scarcely be attempted by way of a brief and simple statement about Plato's metaphysics. It is not an easy doctrine, and it is open to the suspicion that what it says does not make sense. In the eleventh century in Europe the difficulties were realized and a school of thinkers arose who stated their belief that Plato's ideal Forms did not exist at all but were mere names. To those men, whom we now call nominalists, Plato's account of the world gave an illusion of knowing far more than we do. These forerunners of many later thinkers who have purged philosophy of unwarrantable assumptions, the nominalists, were naturally in conflict with the faithful followers of Plato for whom the ideal Forms were real. There existed therefore a considerable conflict between the nominalist and realist schools, and there is no doubt that the issue was felt to be an extremely important one. In the end the nominalists triumphed over the realists and Plato's philosophy ceased to be influential. By this time, however, other events had taken place which in any case meant that for centuries to come Christian thought would be more influenced by the great Greek philosopher Aristotle than by his master Plato.

This is a difficult matter to summarize, but broadly speaking it is true to say that from the thirteenth to the sixteenth century European thought was profoundly affected by the writings of Aristotle. These were at first available only in part in their original Greek form, many of the treatises being available only in Arabic translations. We have to remember that for quite three centuries Arabic works in mathematics, chemistry, physics and astronomy were of great importance and were studied by the leading European thinkers. First Arabic translations, and then the Greek originals of many of Aristotle's works became available and these had momentous effect on men who had previously concerned themselves only with Aristotle's logic. For Aristotle had been the greatest mind in ancient Greece. Some of his biological studies are scientific work of a high order, while even his relatively unsuccessful attempts to understand phenomena which come under the headings of mechanics and physics show a mind at work which was not inclined to the lofty generalizations of Plato. Aristotle certainly tried to get to grips with things as they are, and not as they may be conceived to be in some obscure realm of 'being'. The Arab thinkers, who took so much from him, often introduced their own entirely new conceptions, which in some cases can be seen to be misconceptions of Aristotle's original ideas. In this way they had a certain effect by changing, in some particulars, the motive of scientific inquiry. As yet there was, indeed, very little true science, and much that borders on fancy and speculation. But we can see that the Arab thinkers were a little different from the Greek in temperament and outlook. They were much more practically minded, much more inclined to consider the uses to which knowledge could be applied. The Arabs acknowledged experiment and they did much for chemistry. About the experiments done by the Greeks we have much less information, chiefly, it seems, because they were more theoretical and did not consider that experiments need be recorded. But the Arab influence was by no means altogether fortunate. They sought power over nature, and this desire was so strong that it intensified in many of them those age-old notions about magic and occult influences which can be traced in alchemy and astrology from very early times.

Curiously enough, one part of Arab philosophy that made it so repugnant to Christian thinkers was really that part of it which seems to us most in accord with a modern scientific point of view. Although the details were often fantastic, there was a conviction in certain Arabic writers, especially in Averroes (1126–98), that events in nature are all determined by the chains of events that lead up to them. This was a deterministic and not a teleological point of view, and as such it was clearly a travesty of the teachings of Aristotle to whom the Arabs referred as their great authority. It was because Aristotle's newly discovered works were proving so influential in the thirteenth century that Christian thinkers set themselves the task of grappling with them. And in this way arose that system of medieval thought which was worked out with such thoroughness, such regard for logic and rationality, that when it was completed men not unnaturally believed that they had reckoned with all the great problems and had, in the new systematized teaching, an answer to all the questions that really mattered. Indeed when scientific inquiries were intensified they seemed to many of the best minds of the time to be dubious practices, taking men outside the intellectual limits which could be properly accepted. Much of the writing of the great astronomer

Kepler, not to mention the outpourings of a Paracelcus, strike the modern student of science as repugnant to a degree. Such occultism or obscurantism is, we should feel, exactly the sort of nonsense that science disproves. Something of the same sort may have been felt by the intellectual cleric of the sixteenth or early seventeenth century when acquainted with some new and apparently fantastic claim of the science of the time.

The working out of a satisfactory philosophy of nature took centuries. We can understand this better if we realize that science and its appropriate philosophy had to be discovered at the same time, and that for centuries there were only fitful successes to illuminate the path. There were many schools of thought about Aristotle's doctrine in the Middle Ages. When his views were expounded in the thirteenth century their influence throughout Christendom was to exalt the place of logic and to treat all change as the process by which what was potential became actual, much as the potentiality of becoming an oak tree may be said to exist in the acorn. Mathematics was logically divorced from his conception of a physical explanation because mathematics could in Aristotle's view deal only with abstractions, and for a proper explanation of any event, however simple, many other considerations were needed. It seems distinctly odd to a modern reader that 'physics' could be anything but a mathematical subject. Yet Aristotle considered the subject of physics at length and in his view it was not a mathematical subject. The most significant part of the history of science between the thirteenth and seventeenth centuries lay in the efforts that were made, often obscurely, to introduce mathematics into physics.

There is a strong tendency among historians today to enlarge on the achievements of thirteenth- and fourteenth-century Aristotelians, chiefly in order to correct the rather naïve view, that was once common, that science all began in the sixteenth and seventeenth centuries. In the Christian Church it could never be forgotten that Aristotle was a pagan writer. His philosophy, said Telesio (1508–80), 'knows neither piety nor a creator'. But Telesio's criticisms were also directed against Aristotle because his explanations were not derived from observation. Early in the sixteenth century, however, explanations quite different from those considered by Aristotle began to attract attention. The Greeks associated with Pythagoras had made much of certain discoveries about the properties of numbers. In particular they were fascinated by the idea of numerical series which seemed to possess a deep significance. We know that when a stretched wire is divided in various simple proportions the notes given out can be recognized to be connected with the musical scale. This sort of relation typifies the sort of discovery which became specially valued. The new emphasis on mathematics influenced Copernicus; it may even be said to be the mainspring of his great work of 1543 on the geometry of the solar system.

When we approach the task of saying, as simply as possible, what Copernicus, or Kepler, or Galileo did we have to see their work against this rather complex background of history. From the thirteenth to the sixteenth century Aristotelian and Arabic works were immensely important in Europe. To a considerable extent they determined in advance what sort of scientific studies would be possible and in what terms conclusions would be expressed. It looks very much as if, within such a framework, an impasse might have been reached, so restricted were the principles that seemed to be most important.

But we must not forget that the Arabs were good mathematicians and we must not neglect that tradition derived from Pythagoras and Plato which Aristotle's work had so long pushed into the background. It was indeed the mathematical part of this older tradition which was to prove significant. In the universities of northern Italy mathematicians went back to the study of old problems dating from the time of Pythagoras and his followers. In a way that now looks haphazard and accidental some of these ideas filtered through to northern Europe. Copernicus, the originator of our modern planetary system, studied in Italy and returned to pursue, in his spare time, certain mathematical problems connected with astronomy that interested him. Later we find this northern Italian influence affecting scholars in several northern European centres, so that in time the mathematical training of several astronomers was broadened beyond the traditional confines of their subject.

It is well known that Copernicus greatly simplified the theory of the solar system by treating the earth as a planet and not the centre about which all other bodies move. He had before him the example of Aristarchus of Samos (late third century B.C.), who had proposed this in principle. But this detracts nothing from Copernicus's achievements. Copernicus went much farther than Aristarchus into the details of his heliocentric system. The *De Revolutionibus Orbium Coelestium* is comparatively a difficult book, full of geometrical figures and arguments expressed in mathematical form. In this Copernicus was continuing or reviving the tradition of certain Greek thinkers such as Heraclides (fourth century B.C.), Aristarchus (third century B.C.), Eratosthenes (third century B.C.) and Hipparchus (second century B.C.), all of whom had shown a remarkable power to dissociate themselves mentally from the overwhelming influence of what we might call common sense. That is to say they were able to regard the movements of the heavenly bodies as a set of phenomena which should be reducible to order and they accepted this as a complex problem in geometry. Careful observation of the moon, for example, showed the difference between the time this body takes to return to the same position with respect to the sun, and with respect to the fixed stars. This is the difference between the *synodic* month and the *sidereal* month, and it is accounted for by the sun's motion along the ecliptic. Details of this sort could not be disregarded by exact-minded men, and we find in the best work of the Greeks a remarkable effort to show that all the observed facts concerning the planets, the moon, and the sun, were the outcome of a geometrical scheme which defined the motions of these bodies relative to the earth, assuming for this purpose that all motions in the heavens must be based on the circle. In the *Almagest* of the astronomer Ptolemy of Alexandria (to give the work the Arabic title by which it was known in Europe) much of this Greek work was brought together. This book was written during the second century A.D. The Arabs conquered Alexandria as early as A.D. 641 and down to about the middle of the fourteenth century astronomical work continued in various Arabic centres. This caused Greek ideas to be preserved, and there were minor additions by the Arabs themselves. From the earliest times, therefore, up to the sixteenth century when Copernicus encountered the Pythagorean spirit in northern Italy where he went to study, astronomy continued to be a live subject, exacting, and too difficult to be pursued without adequate mathematical training.

Copernicus's own words taken from his famous book on the planetary system, deserve to be quoted here. 'After long study I have reached these conclusions,' he wrote, 'that the sun is a fixed star, surrounded by planets which revolve round it and of which it is the centre and light: that besides the principal planets there are secondary ones revolving, as satellites, round their principals and, with them, round the sun: that the earth is a primary planet subject to a triple motion on its axis and round the sun, by which means I explain the phenomena of diurnal and annual movement, the alternation of the seasons with all the changes of light and temperature that go with them.' With all this, however, Copernicus retained, in all other respects, the view of the universe that was traditional. At the boundary of all the spheres that make up the planetary system was the sphere of the fixed stars revolving now about the sun and not the earth as a centre.

Meanwhile the Aristotelians of the sixteenth century were not idle. It has been shown that some of them became interested in experiments and realized the inadequacy of Aristotle's physics. Going back to William of Ockham in the fourteenth century there was quite a new tradition which encouraged a much more empirical, less abstractly logical, point of view concerning nature's phenomena. Gradually it was borne in on men that there is much in nature that might, after all, have been otherwise. For centuries it had been an article of faith that God had created the only universe that could exist, and because he was omniscient and good, and concerned principally with men's condition, the understanding of nature lay in the perceiving of the ubiquity of moral laws. From the Greeks there came a deep belief that the structure of the world fulfilled, or would in the end fulfil, the purposes inherent in it. There were four primary elements, according to Aristotle, and four qualities, which might be connected with them. The sinking of a stone in water, or the rising of fire upwards, exemplified the law that each element sought its proper place. But all change was limited to that part of the world that lay within the moon's sphere. All heavenly motions were circular, and the successive spheres on which the heavenly bodies moved increased in size as one went from the moon outwards to the planets, the sun, and the sphere of the fixed stars. Beyond the fixed stars was the *Primum Mobile*, the origin of all the motions. All these spheres were in some way able to influence each other's motion, but the region beyond the moon was one of changeless perfection in which no new event could be expected to take place.

The appearance of a brilliant new star in the constellation Cassiopeia, in 1572, must therefore be reckoned important in the history of science. The Danish astronomer Tycho Brahe was attracted to study it, and he was able to show that it did not in fact belong, as it should, to the sublunary sphere. Instead of shuddering at the thought of the divine wrath, or admonition, that the new star might portend we find this young nobleman taking sights on it as accurately as he could, and night after night noting that its position in the heavens appeared unchanged.

'Last year (1572), in the month of November,' he wrote, 'on the eleventh day of that month, in the evening, after sunset, when, according to my habit, I was contemplating the stars in a clear sky, I noticed that a new and unusual star, surpassing the others in brilliancy, was shining almost directly above my head; and since I had, almost from boyhood, known all the stars of the heavens perfectly (there is no great difficulty in attaining that knowledge), it was quite evident to me that there had never before been any star in that place in the sky, even the smallest, to say nothing of a star so conspicuously bright as this. I was so astonished at this sight that I was not ashamed to doubt the trustworthiness of my own eyes. But when I observed that others, too, on having the place pointed out to them, could see that there was really a star there, I had no further doubts. A miracle indeed, either the greatest of all that have occurred in the whole range of nature since the beginning of the world, or one certainly that is to be classed with those attested by the Holy Oracles, the staying of the Sun in its course in answer to the prayers of Joshua, and the darkening of the Sun's face at the time of the Crucifixion. . . .

'It is a difficult matter, and one that requires a subtle mind, to try to determine the distances of the stars from us, because they are so incredibly removed from the earth; nor can it be done in any way more conveniently and with greater certainty than by the measure of the parallax (diurnal), if a star have one. For if a star that is near the horizon is seen in a different place than when it is at its highest point and near the vertex, it is necessarily found in some orbit with respect to which the Earth has a sensible size. How far distant the said orbit is, the size of the parallax compared with the semi-diameter of the Earth will make clear.' [Tycho's explanation comes to this: an object quite near to the earth will not appear in exactly the same position in the heavens when viewed from two places wide apart on the earth's surface, *or* from the same place at certain different times of year. It will, that is, show parallax.] He goes on:

'In order, therefore, that I might find out in this way whether this star was in the region of the Element or among the celestial orbits, and what its distance was from the earth itself, I tried to determine whether it had a parallax, and, if so, how great a one; and this I did in the following way: I observed the distance between this star and Schedir of Cassiopeia (for the latter and the new star were both nearly on the meridian), when the star was at its nearest point to the vertex, being only six degrees removed from the zenith itself (and for that reason, though it were near the Earth, would produce no parallax in that place, the visual position of the star and the real position then uniting in one point, since the line from the centre of the Earth and that from the surface nearly coincide). I made the same observation when the star was farthest from the zenith and at its nearest point to the horizon, and in each case I found that the distance from the above-mentioned fixed star was exactly the same, without the variation of a minute: namely 7 degrees and 55 minutes. Then I went through the same process, making numerous observations with other stars. Whence I conclude that this new star has no diversity of aspect, even when it is near the horizon. For otherwise, in its least altitude it would have been farther away from the above-mentioned star in the breast of Cassiopeia than when in its greatest altitude. Therefore, we shall find it necessary to place this star, not in the region of the Element, below the Moon, but far above, in an orbit with respect to which the Earth has no sensible size. For if it were in the highest region of the air, below the hollow region of the Lunar sphere, it would, when nearest the horizon, have produced on the circle a sensible variation of altitude from that which it held when near the vertex. . . .

'Therefore, this new star is neither in the region of the Element, below the Moon, nor among the orbits of the seven wandering stars, but it is in the eighth sphere, among the other fixed stars, which was what we had to prove.'

Tycho Brahe is not, and does not deserve to be, as famous as Copernicus. To him we can attribute no great intellectual advance or particularly original ideas. Yet his place in the history of astronomy is extremely important since he set an example of accuracy and thoroughness in astronomical observation which was a new thing in the whole history of science. He even made allowances for the estimated errors of his instruments, showing in this a really exceptional quality as a researcher. Yet essentially he was a typical figure of the Renaissance period, eccentric, even bizarre, in his personal history, yet bringing to his astronomical work all the advantages of aristocratic upbringing and connexions, using large sums of money on the construction of his ambitious observatories. From 1576 until well into the seventeenth century Tycho's observatory on the island of Hveen in the Sound off Copenhagen was famous amongst astronomers. Some seven years after the completion of this first observatory called Uraniborg, Tycho built a second observatory known as Stierneborg to the south. Observation was done here in subterranean rooms which had only their roofs above ground: the best solution Tycho could find to the problem of protection against rain and wind. We must remember that the telescope was as yet unknown. All Tycho's observations were made with graduated scales and using the naked eye.

If the new star of 1572 was truly a star, and did not belong to the sublunary sphere (where according to prevalent ideas such phenomena ought alone to arise), then it should not appear to move in relation to the stars. This was found by Tycho to be the case. In 1577 Tycho's interest was attracted by a comet which appeared. He was able to show that this body must be pursuing a path which took it through some of the spheres containing the planets. This was damaging evidence against the old Ptolemaic

Theory. Yet Tycho never accepted Copernicanism, partly because he considered it almost incredible that the massive earth should be moved. There was also the genuine scientific objection that a moving earth, moving in an orbit about the sun, should give rise to *annual* visual displacements, called parallax, among the other heavenly bodies. Attempts to observe this phenomenon were made throughout the seventeenth century by many astronomers, but it was not detected until 1838 owing to its small magnitude. Over this point the men of the seventeenth century divided sharply. Some concluded that the astronomical distances are so great that the effect is microscopic (which is correct), others concluded against the Copernican theory on this negative evidence. In Tycho's system the earth remains at rest and the sun goes round it. Round the sun, however, revolve all the other planets.

Tycho Brahe and Kepler were both educated at northern universities, Tycho at Leipzig and Kepler at the Protestant university of Tübingen. There do not seem to be any grounds for supposing that these centres were backward compared with Italian centres like Bologna, at least so far as mathematics and astronomy were concerned. Rheticus, follower of Copernicus, was associated with Leipzig for some time, while at Tübingen there was Michael Mästlin, a very able astronomer who instructed Kepler in the Copernican theory and turned his thoughts towards astronomy as the subject of his life's work. It seems clear that by the latter part of the sixteenth century the sciences were being developed all over Europe. Many of the teachers had spent years in Italian universities and then settled at northern centres; this seems to be true of the botanists as well as the astronomers and mathematicians.

Kepler (1571–1630) came of a poor family and all his life had financial difficulties. He successively held posts as a mathematician to the Emperor Rudolph of Austria, as a professor at Linz, and for a time he was associated with the military adventurer Wallenstein who made him Professor of Astronomy at Rostock. Kepler was not above casting horoscopes for money when needs were greatest. His great work was done under difficult conditions. The clash between the old empire and the new mercantile states of the north which underlay the opposition of Protestant and Catholic gave rise to conditions of turmoil and insecurity. Kepler was much of his life a wanderer and the story of his life, which included an occasion when he had to defend his mother against a charge of witchcraft, reads strangely when placed side by side with his abstract ideas and mathematical researches. But some of these read strangely also.

At the age of twenty-five Kepler published his first work entitled *Mysterium Cosmographicum*—the mystery of the universe—in which he believed he had discovered an important law of planetary motions. The subject very aptly illustrates the Pythagorean, or neo-Platonic, ideas that appealed forcibly to him. Using the Copernican system he took the distances of the planets from the sun (so far as these were then known) and showed that the five regular solids beginning with the cube could be fitted, as a matter of geometry, into the spaces between the planetary spheres. Both Tycho Brahe and Galileo thought the idea was interesting. The most important consequence was that Tycho Brahe invited the young man to come and work with him at a castle near Prague whither he had removed himself and some of his books and instruments from Denmark. It was then that Tycho bequeathed to Kepler a mass of recorded observations of certain of the planets which he had taken over a great part of their orbits. The first-fruits of this famous collaboration at Prague were the *Rudolphine Tables* of the planets, the publication of which was delayed until 1627. These tables superseded the *Alphonsine Tables* which were based on the ancient Greek system, the work of the astronomer Ptolemy. Tycho died before Kepler could progress far with his next great task, the reconciliation of the planetary tables with Tycho's system.

It is well known that in the end Kepler reconciled the observations not with Tycho's system but with a modified form of Copernicus's system. The method was a prolonged exercise in the use of geometry and as such illustrates the state of science at that time. Kepler had to discover the geometrical shape of the orbit of Mars starting from a number of triangles of known shape, all of them having the line joining the sun and the earth as base line. If a sufficient number of triangles could be drawn in on the plan their apices would fix the general shape of the orbit of the planet.

It was generally supposed that the orbits of heavenly bodies, if not circles, must be the outcome of several circular motions suitably compounded. Great ingenuity was in fact required to make the problems work out in this way, but for centuries this type of system was taken for granted. Kepler began by assuming that Mars had a circular orbit but that the planet revolved with constant angular velocity about a point or 'equant' that was not necessarily at the centre. This was an established idea. But Kepler could make the plan work only by assuming a loose fit of the observations. After all, Tycho Brahe's observations might be in error to the necessary extent of eight minutes of a degree. It was a tribute to his master that Kepler rejected this possibility and persevered until he found an orbit that really agreed closely with the observations. It was one of the most famous of all discoveries, and one of the most famous of the new laws of nature, that the planet Mars goes round the sun in an ellipse, the sun being at one focus. This work took many years of Kepler's life.

In his *Mysterium Cosmographicum* Kepler had speculated on the reason why the speeds of the planets appear to decrease more quickly than their distances increase from the sun. None of the relative distances were then known at all accurately, and the absolute distances were not known at all. Men were very much surprised later in the century when the immense distances of even the nearest planets, and the scale of the solar system, were brought home to them. Kepler in this work imagined that a force, or moving spirit (*anima motrix*), might emanate from the sun and it might be this, as in a mighty whirlpool, that sustained the motions of the planets. This would explain, he thought, why the speeds fall off with increasing distances of a planet from the sun. It was a very mistaken view of the physics of the problem, for it repeated the ancient error of Aristotle whereby moving bodies needed a constant force to maintain their motions. But perhaps this vague notion prevented him from despairing too soon in his years of work on the orbit of Mars.

There are three laws of planetary motion associated with the name of Kepler. The first two were given in his *Astronomia Nova* of 1609, and the third was given in his *Harmonices Mundi* of 1619. They sum up all that was needed to define the elliptical orbits of the planets. No mechanical explanation was given until Newton's *Principia* was published in 1687.

The mathematical work involved in Kepler's studies of the planets was not in itself complicated. And the tediousness of much of the work of astronomers was soon to be reduced through the invention of logarithms published by Napier in 1614. The essence of Kepler's achievement lay in the way he tried to discover what we would today term the right equation. Given a set of observations what form of equation will represent them all, so that if we wish we can *deduce in advance* what new observations are to be expected? This is a characteristic method of physical science. Tycho Brahe and Kepler both used to compare the results of different types of calculation to see which best accorded with the observations. Only later was such a method used in the analysis of experimental results gained in the laboratory. Yet in Kepler's lifetime the great Galileo was making his first trials in this direction. Later in the century Newton's contemporaries were overwhelmed when he showed that what were in effect 'laboratory' laws could in fact apply to the planets. This was certainly a far greater achievement than Kepler's, but Kepler deserves to be remembered because he broke away from the formalism which had governed astronomy from the time of the Greeks. The law that states that a planet pursues an elliptical orbit was shown by Newton to be a consequence of other more fundamental laws. It is therefore derivative. Nevertheless, it was a law in the new sense that the seventeenth century was to recognize. Granted this law the deductions could be compared with observation and they were found to be correct. An important question about scientific method arises here. If, as a nineteenth-century writer put it, 'hypothetical anticipation of nature is an essential part of inductive inquiry', it is to Kepler and Galileo that we must look back, not to Francis Bacon or Descartes who wrote so much more copiously and persuasively about the method by which inquiries should be pursued. What these writers did was to help to destroy for ever the lingering belief in a literary transmission of science, the belief that it is to some learned authority of the past that we must turn for our understanding. During the seventeenth century it dawned on the men who chiefly created modern science that a fresh inquiry was necessary and that authorities were largely useless.

It is an interesting sidelight on the controversies of the early seventeenth century to see what objections Kepler had to Tycho Brahe's system. Writing in 1605 he said (*Johannes Kepler, Life & Letters,* C. Baumgardt, 1952) that one of his main objections was that 'if the sun moves round the earth, then it must, of necessity, along with the other planets, become sometimes faster, sometimes slower in its movement, and this without following fixed courses since there are none. But this is incredible. Furthermore, the sun which is so much higher ranking than the unimportant earth would have to be moved by the earth in the same way as the five other planets are put in motion by the sun. That is completely absurd. Therefore it is much more plausible that the earth together with the five planets is put in motion by the sun and only the moon by the earth.'

There is here an objection to a mathematically improbable state of affairs, and a feeling also for a general physical explanation which, though erroneous, would at least be general in its applications. Kepler did not follow Tycho in supposing the earth to be too vast to be moved. On the contrary he was among the first to suppose that other bodies in the planetary system are much larger. Both Tycho and Kepler are in some senses remote and half-medieval figures seen from our modern point of view, but if there is no denying that Kepler is far in advance of Tycho we must remember that it was Tycho's painstaking labours that gave Kepler his great opportunities. The combined labours of Tycho and Kepler comprise a wonderful chapter in the history of astronomy. That both men were struggling to see things as they are, and not as an ancient authoritative system requires them to be, adds intensely to their interest. Yet inevitably both remained in bondage to many ideas of their time.

We should be mistaken if we thought the decision between the Copernican and Tychonic systems was soon reached. In the nature of things this was not easy, for the Tychonic gave, at least formally, as good an account of the planetary motions as the Copernican. This is the point at which the men of science came up against physical and not mathematical problems. Somewhat later

Robert Hooke in England looked for an *experimentum crucis* which might determine between the two rival systems. Unfortunately many physical effects that might be expected if the earth rotates and is in motion in its orbit proved either to be erroneous or else they were beyond experimental observation with the techniques then available. Hooke was one of the best judges of experiments of his age and he realized that parallactic motions amongst the stars are probably too small to be detected. Thus many adhered to the Copernican system in spite of the absence of a vital piece of evidence.

We must not, of course, forget that the great Galileo threw into the scales his brilliant telescopic observations of 1610 and his equally brilliant discussion of them. This discussion is to be found in his books *Siderius Nuncius* ('Messenger of the Stars'), *Il Saggiatore* which was a discussion of the new methods of science, and, above all, the work he began in 1626, the *Dialogue on the Two Chief Systems of the World* (to give the English title). Galileo, in the first years of the seventeenth century, heard of the invention of the telescope in Holland. Following the clues he received he invented the instrument for himself using, however, a combination of lenses which we now use only in opera glasses: that is, a converging objective of long focal length combined with a diverging eye-piece. This telescope was soon superseded by what was called the Keplerian form in which the eyepiece was a converging lens of short focal length. It is a great advantage of the Keplerian telescope that cross-wires can be mounted in the focal plane of the eye-piece. This turns the telescope from being an observational instrument into one that will also measure. Galileo's telescopes were very limited in power but they enabled him to make important discoveries. Galileo made many telescopes and sent them out with copies of his *Siderius Nuncius* so that in various centres of Europe his observations could be repeated. He corresponded with Kepler and together these two great men decided there could really be no serious opposition any longer to the Copernican system.

What was it that gave them such confidence? A brief statement of Galileo's telescopic observations of 1610 suffices to answer this question, for taken all together the things he saw through his very imperfect telescope constituted convincing evidence for Copernicus's system. The moon is, of course, the most easily observed body in the sky. Galileo saw that its surface was pitted and uneven. There were, he conjectured, mountains very much like those we know on the earth. Much more important, however, were his observations of Jupiter and Venus. For Jupiter had several moons: four could be seen (eleven are known today) and these quite clearly were moving in orbits about the planet. It was like a small solar system. As for Venus, which is seen only briefly after sunset or before dawn because it is so near the sun, this planet shows phases like the moon. In the telescope it shows up brilliantly like a little moon, going through the same crescent shapes as it waxes and wanes. Obviously this must mean that it shines by reflected light just as would be required by the Copernican system, while its orbit about the sun could be readily accommodated to that system along with those of all the other known planets.

The discovery of sunspots, and of the nature of the Milky Way, which also date from this time, do nothing of themselves to prove that Copernicus was right, Kepler right, and all the old authorities wrong. But they opened up new horizons, they suggested that much remained to be discovered. Indeed evidence was coming from various sources to suggest that the universe is indeed vast and our earth merely a planet among others, our sun a star among others.

Written from very different standpoints, it is true, the various accounts that have come down to us from the philosophers and men of science of the first part of the seventeenth century all combine to give a powerful impression of the intellectual revolution that was taking place. We must not forget, in such a short essay, that the period from Copernicus to Kepler in astronomy can be matched by the period from Vesalius to Harvey in medicine. Here again we have an ancient tradition of great importance in human affairs which was early affected by the growing independence of mind to be found at this time. There are important philosophical reasons why the physical sciences took precedence in the seventeenth century, so that in the early eighteenth century there were complaints that 'mathematics have engrossed all' and that there was no room for the biological sciences.

In Andreas Vesalius (1515–64) we have a man who can well

be compared with Copernicus. A Belgian physician and student of anatomy, he is famous for his book *De humani corporis fabrica* which came out in 1543, the same year as Copernicus's masterpiece. This book, remarked Singer and Rabin in their *Prelude to Modern Science*, 'opens a new scene as with the quick rise of a curtain, for it is suddenly, essentially and brilliantly modern'. Anatomy was the first observational subject to be studied on modern scientific lines, and Vesalius's book with its fine illustrations dates the beginning of modern scientific work in this field. He could never have achieved his aim, Vesalius, said in his preface 'had I not put my own hand to the business': a sentiment that would have seemed rash and irresponsible to the more slavish followers of Galen. Yet Vesalius was for many years himself a follower of the great Greek physician and the violence of his denunciation of the ancient authorities must have been the result of a drastic change in his convictions. When we come to the work of William Harvey we find this very clear statement which could well be applied to so much of the new work that was then going on. 'I profess to learn and teach anatomy,' he wrote, 'not from books, but from dissections; not from positions of philosophers, but from the fabric of nature.'

We must not hasten on without perceiving the lesson that Kepler and others of this period learned so painfully, for it is a lesson that is still not widely understood. Fortunately it can be expressed in very general terms and they are as follows. The prescientific mentality tended to assume that in essence the explanations of things rested on argument and to a very large extent could be known in advance. Even the Greeks never quite got away from this predilection. They assumed that circles and straight lines were enough to account for all natural movements. Kepler's experience was critical because he found himself compelled by the evidence to accept an ellipse. This is the chief lesson to be learned at this stage: the explanation of phenomena may turn out to be quite different from what we expect. Indeed what we expect may have to be explicitly denied. A scientist may go further and say 'Our expectations have really very little to do with the truth about things. Most if not all human expectations have been proved false. This is a process that may not have an end.'

CHAPTER TWO

The Mathematician

THE studies of mathematicians, and the outlook engendered by an ancient tradition which goes back to the Pythagoreans of ancient Greece, provide an important part of the explanation of the rise of Western science. Yet the character and outlook of the sixteenth-century mathematician present difficulties for the modern student. One of the most enlightened, Franciscus Vieta (1540–1603) was brought up to be a lawyer in Paris and spent many years in public life. After 1580 he gave up most of his leisure to mathematics and his great work *In Artem Analyticam Isagoge* was published in 1591. In this he explained how algebra could be applied to the solution of geometrical problems.

It is of interest that the King of France, Henry IV, interested himself in his distinguished mathematician and got him to answer a mathematical challenge from his countryman Adrian Romanus. Right up to the eighteenth century challenges to solve peculiarly difficult problems were common. They provided one of the chief means of communication between mathematicians who were almost all of them amateurs and devoted to interests far more recondite than the demands on mathematics made by commerce, banking, navigation or astronomy. Henry IV got Vieta to decipher a code used by the Spanish for their dispatches at this time. So convinced was Philip II that this code could not be deciphered that when he found the French knew his plans he complained to the Pope that sorcery was being used against him (W. W. Rouse Ball, *Short Account of the History of Mathematics*). Vieta's works were published for private circulation. They were later collected and printed in an edition due to the Dutch mathematician van Schooten in 1646. An explanation of their contents is somewhat technical but it can be said that they provide a foundation for all subsequent developments in algebra and contributed also to the completion of elementary trigonometry which from this time onwards was familiar to all mathematicians.

Vieta was a mathematician and not a scientist. Looking back to the Greeks, mathematics before Vieta was almost invariably concerned with abstract problems arising out of the properties of numbers or of geometrical figures. There had been two great periods in all these centuries: that associated with the Greeks (Pythagoreans, the schools of Cyzicus and Athens, and the Alexandrians of the third century B.C.), and, much later, the far smaller contributions of Hindu and Arabic writers which are nevertheless important because they introduced our modern numerals and greatly improved mathematical notation. European mathematics, broadly speaking, revived only in the sixteenth century. With writers like Descartes, Fermat and Newton in the seventeenth century we step into modern times. We then find most mathematicians deeply interested in science.

The sixteenth century is of peculiar interest just because the penetration of physics by mathematics was such a difficult thing to understand. In the seventeenth century, after Galileo, we find the matter understood by the leading men of the time. Before this we get the impression that even some of the best minds failed to distinguish between rational matters and irrational mysteries. The court mathematician might be called on to calculate an orbit according to the Ptolemaic system, to correct the calendar, or decipher a code. But he might equally well be required to cast a horoscope and predict days that would be propitious for special events. The result was that the sixteenth century mathematician was sometimes an obscure personage, or one given over to fantastic ideas. Even the most sober accounts of the life of Girolamo Cardan (1501–76) seem preposterous. 'A gambler, if not a murderer', remarks Rouse Ball, he divided his time as a Professor at Pavia in Northern Italy 'between debauchery, astrology, and mechanics'. After imprisonment for publishing a horoscope of Christ he was employed in his last years as astrologer to the papal court. 'This proved fatal to him, for, having foretold that he should die on a particular day, he felt obliged to commit suicide in order to keep up his reputation—so at least the story runs.' Yet Cardan did some genuinely good work in mathematics and was well versed in the scientific and mechanical experiments of his age.

The tradition that the greatest Greek mathematicians bequeathed to Europe concerned geometry above all else. Indeed, as we shall see, geometry alone seemed to them to provide an escape from the 'irrational' in mathematics, using this word in a special sense, and this point of view persisted right up to the time of Newton. Pythagoras brought into mathematics the notion of *proof*. It was his greatest achievement. Before him geometry 'had been largely a collection of rules of thumb empirically arrived at without any clear indication of the mutual connections of the rules, and without the slightest suspicion that all were deducible from a comparatively small number of postulates. Proof is now so commonly taken for granted as the very spirit of mathematics that we find it difficult to imagine the primitive thing that must have preceded mathematical reasoning.' (E. T. Bell, *Men of Mathematics*.)

Yet while Greek geometry as a whole had this character problems were discovered, by Pythagoras himself, as well as others, that have remained perplexing right down to modern times. We have today an extensive literature on these philosophical matters but at the time they seemed to threaten the whole rational foundation of the subject. The legendary brotherhood of the Pythagoreans was guilty of credulous mysticism in regard to certain numerical relationships and Plato followed them in this weaker side of their work. Why, for example, should six be a 'perfect' number because it happens to be the sum of the numbers which are its prime factors ($6=1+2+3$)? Why should ten be an ideal, number because it is, for one thing, the sum of the integers 1, 2, 3, 4? Yet because ten is such an ideal number it was argued that there must be ten moving bodies in the heavens. Because the Pythagoreans could account for only nine, counting the sun, earth, moon, and the known planets, they concluded there must be another body which remained invisible. This sort of reasoning, if it be called such, is easily extended, or linked up with credulous and irrational teachings of which there has never been any serious lack in the world. In astrology and in the so-called Cabbala which influenced quite able men in the sixteenth century we find a mass of irrational ideas the toleration of which marked off very roughly the medieval from the modern period. It is much the same in the history of alchemy. Working in symbols, as mathematicians do, requires a certain quality of mind which is not found in everyone. There was a temptation, so long as astrology flourished, for mathematicians to exploit their gifts and trade on the credulity of princes, possibly as a compensation for the miserable rewards they were then paid. Nor perhaps did such men as Leonardo da Vinci in the fifteenth and sixteenth centuries know themselves where rational relationships in natural phenomena began and ended. Astrology and astronomy were long treated as one subject, so that valid mathematical or scientific work was intermingled with what seems to us pure charlatanism.

Yet mathematics more than anything else created modern science. From about the time of Kepler it is unmistakable that there was a conviction that there are laws of nature of a special kind and that they are simple enough to be represented exactly in the form of mathematical relationships. It is not the case that vast numbers of experiments were performed and that looking at the results scientists of the seventeenth century reached great natural laws by a process of inductive reasoning. 'The nature of scientific activity as envisaged by the Renaissance thinkers is often incorrectly understood,' remarks a modern writer (Morris Kline, *Mathematics in Western Culture*). 'Many people credit the rise of modern science to the introduction of experimentation on a large scale and believe that mathematics served only occasionally as a handy tool. The true situation . . . was actually quite the reverse. The Renaissance scientist approached the study of nature as a mathematician: that is, he sought and expected to find broad, profound, inimitable, rational principles either through intuition or immediate sense perception, in much the same way as Euclid presumably found his axioms.' As was remarked at the end of Chapter One, expectations must be treated with caution. They can never be entirely eliminated. All we can say is that scientific expectation often stretches the imagination quite severely. In England, certainly, we seem to have suffered from an excess of the influence of Francis Bacon. Great writer as he was Bacon deserves to be remembered as one of the rebellious critics of medieval modes of thinking, and as a visionary. Unfortunately his visions were misleading as a guide to the new mentality. The inarticulate quality of the mathematicians and scientists which has prevented most of them from explaining what their work was about has more than anything contributed to the dualism of our culture. So that a great historian of science has concluded that the great division of mankind is that which marks off those who understand and use scientific methods from those who do not. This difference, if it did not rest so solidly on mathematics, would be much more easily removed, and because it is not seen to be at root mathematical is underestimated.

Next to astronomy the studies of optics, which were more dependent than most others on the performing of experiments, played an important part in the history of science. The reasons for this, which have been well given by A. C. Crombie in his book *Augustine to Galileo*, can be found in part in the theory that light according to an ancient tradition, was the clue to the reality of the universe. Certain influential Arab writers, like Averroes, worked out a theory that came originally from neo-platonic sources which means that every material thing possesses a 'common corporeity'. This apparently has something to do with its being extended in space. For Descartes, we should remember, the essence of matter is that it is extended in space, it is the *res extensa*. For him, also, as we shall see, light had a special interest. Between the thirteenth and seventeenth centuries the subject of optics assumed proportions that we cannot easily understand today. We treat light as a form of energy having no special causative or formal properties, certainly not such as would provide a clue to the whole nature of the universe, and in this we have broken with a tradition that was always more mystical than scientific. We shall see that in effect Newton's great *Principia* of 1687 overthrew the philosophizing of Descartes and brought about a separation of science from the problems of metaphysics which has lasted ever since.

But while it lasted, the persuasion that optics was more than a technical study (such as we require for the design of lenses) was of considerable significance. It greatly extended the range of mathematics. Optics was clearly, in many respects, a geometrical study: the rays of light not only travel in straight lines, they are refracted by lenses, and form images, in such manner as brings all classical geometry to its study. From Roger Bacon in the thirteenth century, to Kepler in the sixteenth, and finally to Descartes, Huygens and Newton in the seventeenth we can trace an extremely important application of mathematics in the search for natural laws, and the extremely detailed application of those laws, such as no other subject except mechanics can offer. Descartes was the last great thinker to attempt a synthesis of all science so as to produce a complete, interconnected, and rational account of the whole universe. It was a grandiose attempt, not without its excitement and fascination, but it failed. Newton's maxim *Hypotheses non fingo,* 'I do not make hypotheses' was in a sense its, epitaph, the title of his great book *The* Mathematical *Principles of Natural Philosophy* striking the note of all great work in the physical sciences since his day. There is a story, which may well be true, that as he turned the pages of Descartes's account of his 'system' he said 'error' several times and put the book down. Henceforth the character of all physical science was to be that it should not exhibit 'error' through the conflict of what was maintained with what could be measured and calculated.

Nothing so ambitious as a summary of the history of mathematics up to the seventeenth century can be attempted in a short chapter of a book written for non-specialists. Yet we need to look at some of the chief ideas which had become common property by the end of the sixteenth century. We may then see more satisfactorily how the great scientists of the seventeenth century went about their work and we may to some extent understand better the nature of modern science also.

All beginnings are of course arbitrary. But the ideas about numbers that we associate with Pythagoras and his followers provide a commonly accepted origin of our subject. 'All things are number' has long been a way of summing up the Pythagorean philosophy. This is ambiguous enough, but the statement does briefly represent their faith—for that was itself ambiguous. It seems clear that from the notion of counting, and from the simplest relations of adding and factorizing, the Pythagoreans went as far as finding the square roots of numbers and thus made a capital, though dismaying, discovery. The whole universe representing, in their view, the interplay of numbers (which are always whole numbers, or integers), it should follow that between any two numbers there must be a rational, if occasionally, complicated relationship. All their early work inclined them to take this for granted much as it is taken for granted by children in a primary school today. Quite clearly they had totally insufficient reasons for their assumption. Pythagoras's theorem about the hypotenuse of a right-angled triangle revealed that this was so. In this theorem the square on the hypotenuse is equal to the sum of the squares on the other two sides. Most people today learn this without excitement, and perhaps without enthusiasm. But for Pythagoras himself it was catastrophic in certain of its consequences. Let us see how this comes about.

In a right-angled isosceles triangle the sides may be represented as having the lengths one unit, one unit, and x units (the hypotenuse). This then means that

$$x^2 = 1^2 + 1^2$$
$$= 2$$

and thus

$$x = \sqrt{2}$$

To the Pythagoreans, with their conviction that 'all is number', a straight line of two units length can be subdivided at any point and a number can be exactly assigned to the length marked off. The square root of 2 is, however, no such quantity. We can never say precisely and finally where it is located on the line since the square root in our modern terminology does not 'come out' as a decimal quantity, nor does it 'recur'. The same difficulty can be expressed in more general terms by taking the sides of the triangle to be x, x and y units of length.

Then

$$y^2 = x^2 + x^2$$
$$= 2x^2$$

and

$$y = \sqrt{2x^2}$$

If this is so y and x cannot both be whole numbers. Consequently, as Pythagoras himself saw, the attempt to understand the world as the outcome of the properties of numbers is doomed to failure since such a number as $\sqrt{2}$ is 'irrational'.

By keeping to geometrical figures, however, the use of 'irrationals' can be in a sense avoided. If we are asked to find the value of $3 \times \sqrt{2}$ the exact answer cannot be given *numerically*. Nevertheless we can easily construct an oblong which, considered in imagination, has exactly these sides, and whose area is therefore exactly the answer we are seeking. Here lies the preference for geometrical methods of working and the origin of the suspicion that was long attached to algebraic methods. In the third century B.C. Euclid collected together and systematized most of what was known of geometry and from that time forth the grand tradition of mathematics remained geometrical. In Euclid all the constructions must be performed with the use of a straight edge and compasses only: a restriction that is not really logical but is due to Plato's great influence, for straight lines and circles in his view were the only ones which were philosophically admissible. It is well known that in Plato's time the apparent movements of the planets could not be reduced to circular motion alone and he set this problem of 'saving the appearances' to the geometers who followed him. The solution offered by Eudoxus, one of Plato's pupils, required a complex arrangement of spheres arranged concentrically but with each successive axis of revolution inclined to the one that preceded it (a detailed description need not be given). It was superseded by the system worked out by Hipparchus (second century B.C.) which rested on the use of epicycles and eccentrics—devices which 'save the appearances' by the use of circles by rather a narrow margin. It was Hipparchus's scheme which was adopted in Ptolemy's *Almagest,* the bible of astronomers up to the end of the sixteenth century. This was as near as the Greek geometers and astronomers came to the discovery of natural law. Had they not limited themselves as they did, the work of Apollonius (third century B.C.) on conic sections, giving us the curves we know as the ellipse, parabola and hyperbola, might have been admitted into their theories. In this case it is hard to avoid the conclusion that Kepler as well as Copernicus might have been anticipated. We must, however, remember that Kepler could not have done his work without Tycho Brahe, and the Greek equivalent of Tycho Brahe appears never to have existed.

For the Greek genius was essentially intellectual and imaginative, not painstakingly practical and laborious. The setting up of one of Tycho Brahe's great metal mural quadrants, and the recording night after night of planetary positions, seems out of accord with their temperament and inclination. Plato expressly denied that observation of the heavens seriously mattered and he questioned whether it would not be a hindrance in the pursuit of truth. We see the Greek mind at work more characteristically in the attempts which were made to solve the three great classical problems of the schools of Athens and Cyzicus: those known as 'squaring the circle', 'trisecting an angle' and 'duplicating the cube'.

To 'square the circle' means constructing, with ruler and compasses only, a square having exactly the area of a given circle. Interesting attempts at this were made by Hippocrates of Chios, Hippias, and Archimedes, but they all failed in their objective, so that at best the answers are approximations. The reason for this is now known, as is the reason for failure in the other two problems: they cannot be done with ruler and compasses alone. They can, however, readily be done with slightly more complicated instruments.

Nevertheless the limitations of the Euclidean tradition in geometry provide also a great example of the success of the human reason when it is set the task of deriving results in a strictly ordered and logical way from a number of accepted postulates. The creation of Euclidean geometry, says Morris Kline, 'engendered a rational spirit. No other human creation has demonstrated how much knowledge can be derived by reasoning alone as have the hundreds of proofs in Euclid. The deduction of these numerous and profound results taught the Greeks and later civilizations the power of reason and gave them confidence in what could be achieved by this faculty.' (*Mathematics in Western Culture.*)

We should not forget that it was Euclid who showed that there are five, and no more than five, regular solids, namely the tetrahedron, the octahedron, the cube, the dodecahedron and the icosahedron. The first two and the last have equilateral triangles for each face of the solid, the third has square faces, and the fourth has each face a regular pentagon. The faces meet along straight lines as edges and there are no curved surfaces or lines. One might suppose that a regular solid could be formed on the basis of a regular hexagon but it is not so; nor can other regular polygons with seven or more sides be employed. We can now see a little more clearly perhaps why Kepler was so excited by his supposed discovery that the five regular solids gave a clue to the constitution of the planetary system. In fact he was wildly mistaken. With the correct distances between the orbits the regular solids do not fit at all well, and there are in addition other planets besides those which were known to him. We should be able to appreciate a little better, however, the nature of Kepler's aims. The laws of nature, if they are not to prove extremely complex, might have a simplicity of this geometrical sort. At that time who could tell? Apollonius's conic sections proved, in the event, to be of greater significance than Plato's circles but mathematicians find no difficulty today in imagining other answers that might be found to the problems set in the study of phenomena. And again and again a mathematical anticipation has proved to have an interesting sequel, although in modern times geometry has receded and relationships of the type treated by 'the calculus' have largely taken their place.

The Greeks were so thoroughly geometrical that a product obtained by multiplying four or more numbers together appears to have been beyond their imagination. When any three numbers, rational or irrational, are multiplied together, the result can be visualized as a three-dimensional figure. Not so the product of four or more numbers. Geometry is, accordingly, not a very suitable preparation for the mathematics which is required in physics, for we have no *a priori* reasons for supposing that its limits correspond to the limits of nature conceived as a 'system'. This, however, seems to be the reason why so many 'systems' were tried at one time or another. Even today geometry retains great importance in one great field of science: cosmology. When the layman reads of 'the expanding universe', or the 'bending' of light rays in gravitational fields, and occasionally hears of non-Euclidean geometries, he is reminded that the great intellectual quest of the Greeks has not really been abandoned.

Fortunately for the workers of the seventeenth century algebra was developed by certain mathematicians of the Arabian school so that new mathematical methods such as Descartes's co-ordinate geometry and above all the differential calculus became possible. The seventeenth century saw a much closer union between mathematics and what we should call mechanics or physics, and the greatest scientists of the time combined in one person the interests of scientific inquiry and great mathematical ability. Even though it was long the fashion to retain methods of geometrical proof much of the new work was in fact done by 'analysis', that is the employment of algebraic equations of one degree or another. Huygens amongst the seventeenth-century scientists was so imbued with the geometrical spirit (and was in his youth called the young Archimedes) that he never made much use of analysis. But Newton developed analysis very drastically and then subsequently published his results in a geometrical form which scarcely even appears to belong to them. That he went to this enormous trouble was because there were still doubts about the validity of some of the new methods. And besides, Huygens had much influence and Newton admired his work very greatly.

Broadly speaking algebra was created by Italian mathematicians of the Renaissance period building on the very important work they inherited from Arab writers of whom Alkarismi (ninth century) is the most famous. The word algebra, meaning 'restoration', comes from the title of Alkarismi's book. In this work Alkarismi gave rules for solving quadratic equations and dealt with related matters including certain types of square roots. Algebra, Arabic numerals and a decimal system reached Europe through the makers of calendars, and merchants who traded with the East, as well as in scientific works that reached the West in various roundabout ways. Renaissance students drew on a wide variety of sources; Latin commentaries, Arabic works, newly discovered Greek texts and a variety of translations of them. Mathematicians of the Renaissance period, says Rouse Ball, 'had barely assimilated the knowledge obtained from the Arabs, including their translations of Greek writers, when the refugees who escaped from Constantinople after the fall of the Eastern empire brought the original works and the traditions of Greek science into Italy. Thus by the middle of the fifteenth century the chief results of Greek and Arabian mathematics were accessible to European students.'

Nor must we forget the influence of printing in this spread of mathematics. The first book on arithmetic to be printed came from the printing press at Treviso near Venice in 1478. This explained the system of Arab numerals, and the positioning systems for hundreds, thousands, etc. From this time onwards we can reckon with the growing importance of mathematics in everyday life and a rise, in time, of the standard of mathematical education. In place of (or rather in addition to) challenges from mathematicians, and privately circulated results, there was soon to be a flow of mathematical treatises, and in the mid-seventeenth century the new journals, published at regular intervals, for the presentation of scientific and mathematical papers.

Much the best illustration of the rising importance of mathematics in the civilization of the late sixteenth century is to be found in the life and work of Simon Stevin (1548–1620), a Dutchman whose fame has always suffered through his being overshadowed by the great Galileo. The historian George Sarton has remarked that he was 'the most original man of the second half of the sixteenth century' and this appears just when we consider his writings, which deal with problems of pure and applied mathematics and extend to navigation, the use of sluices and their employment in defensive warfare, the equilibrium of ships and the layout of military camps to mention only a few matters. Stevin published the first printed tables of interest charges for use by bankers and in every way open to him he stimulated the use of mathematics in practical affairs. The manuscripts of his lessons for Prince Maurice of Nassau were carried by the Prince on his campaigns. On one occasion he lost them and this caused him to have them published in Dutch, Latin and French editions (of which only the first two were printed complete).

Stevin was not only a first-class mathematician, he was also an excellent civil engineer, with a conviction that the mathematical teaching at the engineering school attached to Leyden University should be in the national language and not in Latin. Within the range of mathematics he included several studies we should now treat independently: geography, astronomy, statics and optics. In statics, or the study of bodies at rest through the equilibrium of the forces acting, he made a noteworthy contribution.

A force is a *vector* quantity. This means that we must state its direction as well as its magnitude. When two forces act simultaneously at the same point we cannot as a rule merely add or subtract them—only if they are acting in the same straight line. There is a rule called the parallelogram of forces which enables us to find the effect of the forces and show the magnitude and direction of the 'resultant' force. Thus, if F_1 and F_2 act simultaneously in the

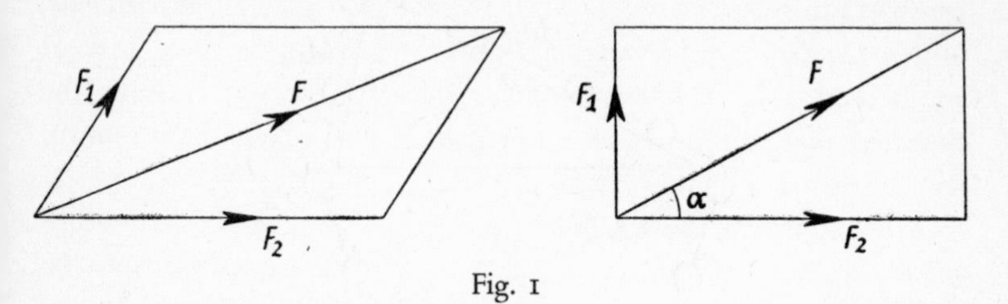

Fig. 1

directions shown (Fig. 1), the resultant force is F, represented by the diagonal of the parallelogram. If F_1 and F_2 happen to be at right angles we have the following simple relations:

$$F_1 = F \sin \alpha$$
$$F_2 = F \cos \alpha$$

(The earliest known use of these trigonometrical terms was in 1626.) It also follows, of course, that a force F in the direction shown can be imagined to be composed of the two component forces F_1 and F_2. If a rope is used to pull a barge along a canal we know that the horse must walk along the bank and so pull the rope a little sideways. To keep the barge going in the right direction use must be made of the tiller. The effective force is not the force F in the rope but the component $F \cos \alpha$. This propels the barge.

Now in the sixteenth century the idea of a force had not been properly clarified, but the difficulties were much less in statical than they were in dynamical problems. From the time of Jordanus Nemorarius, a twelfth- or thirteenth-century writer about whom little is known, there were attempts to work out a treatment of certain problems which today we should describe as the combination and resolution of forces. We have to be cautious, therefore, in expressing work of that time in modern terms. Stevin succeeded in establishing the parallelogram rule for the combination of two forces in quite an ingenious manner. More correctly he established the rule for the special case of two forces acting at right angles.

Imagine, he says, a kind of chain made of a series of small weights, all equal and equally spaced on a light thread, and place this as shown on the two inclined planes *a* and *b* (Fig. 2). Stevin

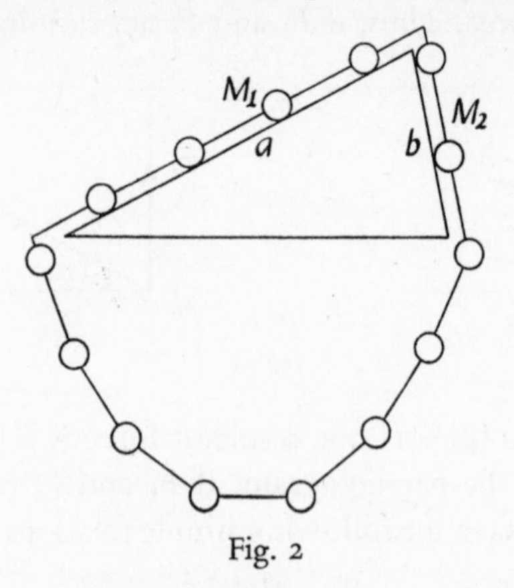

Fig. 2

supposed that *a* and *b* were such that they were exactly proportional to the total weights M_1 and M_2. It is simpler to imagine the system of weights being replaced by a smooth chain and then this particular restriction does not arise.

Now we know, says Stevin, that such a chain will not move. If it did, one way or the other, there would be no change in the distribution of weights and if there were motion there would be no reason to expect it to stop. Since, however, we know that *perpetual motion does not occur* we must conclude that such a system must be in equilibrium. It seemed self-evident to Stevin that the hanging portion shown in Fig. 2 could be cut off at the two ends with-

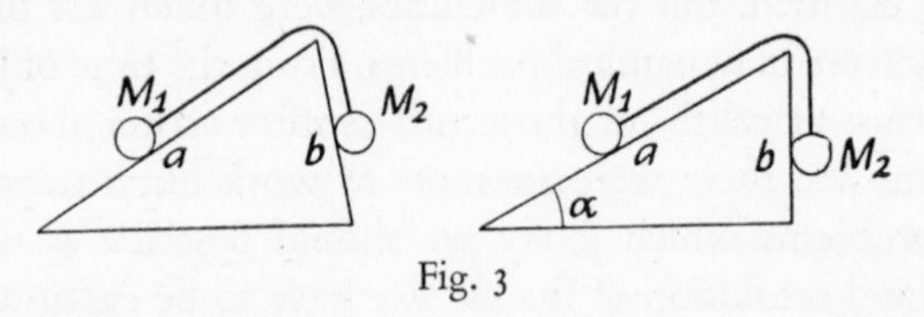

Fig. 3

out disturbing the equilibrium. If this is so a weight M_1 lying on the plane *a* 'balances' a weight M_2 lying on the plane *b*. The numerical relationship is:

$$\frac{M_1}{M_2}=\frac{a}{b}$$

For brevity we need not follow quite the line of reasoning used by Stevin. He saw that there was no reason why the plane b should not be vertical. In this special case there is a purely trigonometrical connexion between a and b which is:

$$b = a \sin \alpha$$

Thus: $$\frac{M_1}{M_2} = \frac{a}{b} = \frac{a}{a \sin \alpha}$$

Therefore: $$M_2 = M_1 \sin \alpha$$

Alternatively $$M_2 = M_1 \cos \beta \quad (\text{where } \beta = 90 - \alpha)$$

This clearly means that a force $M_1 \cos \beta$ acts in the thread. If the thread were severed we should say that $M_1 \cos \beta$ is the force which accelerates the mass down the plane (but this is to introduce ideas which came later).

Stevin believed his study of the inclined plane was one of his best achievements. He gave the diagram showing the inclined planes and their systems of weights on the title page of his book of 1586 and repeated it in a work bearing the date 1608. He was a versatile man and in a full account of his work much space would be needed to discuss his studies of the pressures set up by liquids. Yet for such a gifted man his position was never particularly secure or well rewarded. It seems that it was his close association with Prince Maurice that made much of his work possible. Some of his writings, including a book on social and political matters, his *Vita Politica,* went through several editions and in his day he was undoubtedly influential. He was no remote academically-minded student but rather a man of affairs who turned his mind to many practical problems. The only extant copy of one of his most important publications in pure mathematics was lost when the university library of Louvain was destroyed in the war in 1914. Fortunately the text was preserved in other editions of Stevin's work.

The mathematician, therefore, always an amateur and not at this time a professional, has been an extremely important figure in the history of science. It is essential to refer to his labours as a sort of prelude to the work of the seventeenth century. We find professional mathematicians at work in the seventeenth century. They could then earn their incomes without doing horoscopes and their investigations were strictly rational. With the founding of scientific societies mathematicians and scientists could meet each other and with these greatly increased opportunities for exchanging ideas the rate of progress was much increased. As might be expected in such a subject the relation of master to pupil was always of great importance, one good teacher having an influence that might easily appear out of all proportion to his own originality. But it was the interplay of mathematics with science which is such a striking feature of the seventeenth century. In Rouse Ball's *Short Account of the History of Mathematics* this point is well brought out in Chapter 4. Here he remarks that five distinct stages in the history of modern mathematics can be traced. *First* of all there was the invention of analytical geometry by Descartes (although others contributed to this also); *secondly*, we have the invention, some thirty years later, of the differential calculus. In the *third* place 'Huygens, following Galileo, laid the foundations of a satisfactory treatment of dynamics, and Newton reduced it to an exact science'. 'In the *fourth* place, we may say that during this period the chief branches of physics have been brought within the scope of mathematics'—although not until the beginning of the nineteenth century was it possible to do this for most physical subjects. '*Fifthly* this period has seen an immense extension of pure mathematics.' While not all these developments can be located in the seventeenth century most of them can be found to have occurred in that period.

Such was the prestige of mathematics in the seventeenth century that we find a great increase in the numbers of its students and we find men whose training had been literary interesting themselves in it, sometimes with mournful consequences. Thomas Hobbes is said to have made the acquaintance of Euclid's Geometry about the age of forty. Waiting in a friend's house he took up the book and became engrossed in it. After reading one of the theorems he was overheard to say 'By God, it is impossible.' It is said that Hobbes's own excursions into mathematics showed, not surprisingly, his own lack of training. But that there were so many students of Euclid, so many enthusiasts for Descartes's teachings, so much interest in the affairs of the scientific societies, was due to the spread of mathematical interest. From being a poor student, preoccupied with strange and remote interests (for even professors of mathematics were very little rewarded or recognized), the mathematician stepped forth in the seventeenth century as a new authority.

France, Holland and England could all claim distinguished mathematicians in the first half of the seventeenth century. The French school was particularly brilliant since it was owing to Descartes and also Fermat that analytical geometry was created. Analytical geometry, wrote John Stuart Mill, 'far more than any of his metaphysical speculations, immortalized the name of Descartes, and contributes the greatest single step ever made in the progress of exact sciences.' This is a strong claim but Mill saw that it was justified by the great developments of the second half of the seventeenth century. The future lay with this development in mathematics from which sprang the differential calculus of Leibnitz and Newton. Huygens, the great Dutch mathematician and man of science, remained loyal in all his work to the Greek tradition. His work was essentially geometrical and was quite early modelled on the example of the great Archimedes, easily the most scientific and 'modern' of the Greeks.

The essential idea of analytical geometry is quite simple to explain. It is in working out the details that the power and economy of the method become clear and unfortunately it is too technical to show how this is done in a book of this kind. Anyone who has become acquainted with the use of co-ordinates in giving map references has, in effect, seen the basis of the geometry Descartes invented. Indeed it is often called co-ordinate geometry.

Today we are very accustomed also to graphs, drawn with references to two *axes* at right angles and commonly described as the x– and y– axes. To any point P then correspond a value of x and y which are its co-ordinates. If P (Fig. 4) is imagined to move, either along an S-shaped curve as shown in the figure, or it might be, along a straight line, the values of x and y will change. How will they change? Descartes made his discovery because he recognized that all we need to define the curve or straight line is the algebraic relationship that holds between x and y. In other words we require the equation to the curve or straight line. If two such equations are given it may be that there are points for which the values of x and y can be the same for both. In this case the curves must intersect as at Q. This point can, however, be found *purely by algebra, and without drawing the curves.* Further than this it became clear to Fermat and others that we can find tangents to curves at any required points by purely analytical methods also.

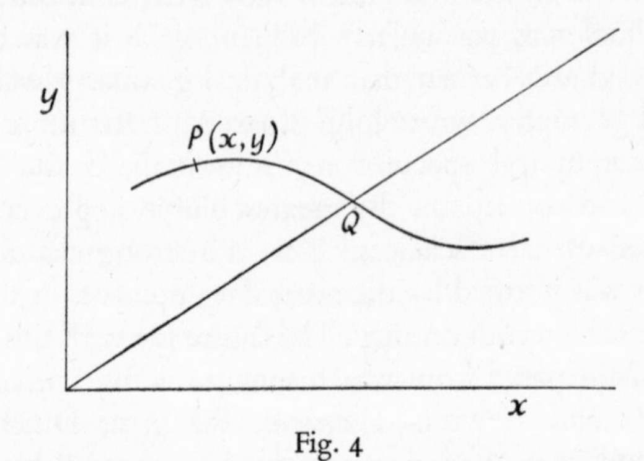

Fig. 4

We can perhaps get a glimpse of the importance of the new developments when we realize that the new curves that became important in seventeenth-century science were all more complicated (that is from the point of view of elementary pure geometry) than the circle. Beside the ellipse (for planetary motion) and the parabola (for projectiles) problems arose giving rise to the rectangular hyperbola, the cycloid, the catenary and many others. Greek methods were not only very cumbersome, they were totally unsuited to finding such things as the varying velocities of bodies in curved paths. On the other hand, given the varying velocities it would not be possible by Greek methods to arrive at the orbit. Then, too, problems were arising when it was necessary to have a method of considering the total effect of a large body, for example in problems about gravity, knowing the law which would operate if the mass were very small indeed. Here, if we have the geometry of the system it should be possible to do the complicated addition sum, not approximately but accurately. For a whole variety of purposes the differential and integral calculus was an urgent requirement and it came through the demonstration by Descartes and Fermat that geometry could be done without diagrams and purely by the use of algebra.

It is quite clear that the men of science of the seventeenth century could scarcely overestimate the importance of mathematics. No longer were such pursuits considered to be of remote intellectual interest only. For the faith that mathematics offered the clue to the laws of nature was found to be vindicated. Thenceforth there is no mistaking the increased effort to reduce problems to mathematical treatment. Lord Brouncker, first President of the Royal Society, was a distinguished mathematician; Isaac Barrow, Newton's tutor at Cambridge, had the advantage of Continental experience (forced on him by political exile) and probably through him Newton acquired a knowledge of analytical geometry. More famous today than Barrow is John Wallis, appointed Savilian Professor of Geometry at Oxford by Cromwell. Wallis deciphered codes for the Parliamentarians during the Civil War. His mathematical writings assisted Newton in his work on the binomial theorem. The age had become a mathematical one. More and more it was realized that exact, mathematical, answers can be given to many problems which had up to that time never been satisfactorily solved. This point of view spread and influenced thought in the remotest spheres, even those, such as politics, where its application seemed inappropriate. Mathematics was turned to use in war, in civil engineering, in the reform of the coinage and many other ways. The new scientific societies became passionately interested in mechanics. The fame of Galileo which spread all over Europe had a good deal to do with this, and in the year, 1642, that Galileo died Isaac Newton was born.

CHAPTER THREE

Rival Philosophies

THE seventeenth century was near enough to medieval times for medieval modes of thought to persist and affect in subtle ways even the best minds of the age. The transition from philosophical to scientific thinking was accomplished only after there had been many disputes, some of them between rival authorities, or between followers of certain philosophers, and some between individual thinkers, and even then it was accomplished only gradually. Sometimes individual thinkers fell foul of authority, as happened to Galileo. Giordano Bruno, a heretical monk, was burned alive in Rome in 1600, but neither he nor Thomasso Campanella, who was imprisoned, can be seen as martyrs for science though they were martyrs for a growing demand for freedom of thought. Science indeed was widely regarded as an appendage to one philosophy or another—it could be claimed by more than one—and conflict with established authority arose more often because of the philosophy than because of the science.

As has been explained, the later Middle Ages inherited teachings which derive from Plato, overlaid with another even more powerful tradition based upon Aristotle's works. In the seventeenth century Aristotelianism was orthodox with the Jesuits, and efforts were made to show that this system could embrace the new science and mathematics and was in fact the true source from which nearly all of it could be traced. It took some particularly striking discovery to disconcert the Aristotelians, but probably they were most notably disturbed in 1672 when for the first time the French astronomers obtained the first reliable measure of the distance of Mars. Mars was then at a near point in its orbit, and from this measurement, by means of Kepler's Laws, the astronomers deduced the distances of the other bodies and the dimensions of the whole solar system. The conclusion that the sun's mean distance from the earth is 87,000,000 miles was of the right order of magnitude, and so were the gigantic masses obtained for the planets. These were shattering blows for the old Aristotelian conceptions and educated men of the time were increasingly inclined for this reason and many others which must be described, to turn to an alternative system which treated the whole of nature in a satisfying way: that of the philosopher Descartes.

It seems clear that all the men of science of the seventeenth century adhered to some general philosophy or other. Very few of them were Aristotelians, but some like Gassendi and Boyle revived the doctrines of Epicurus, especially the atomic doctrine; others like Mersenne followed Galileo; many in England as well as on the Continent, followed Descartes. When Newton's *Principia* was criticized by Huygens and Leibnitz it was not the science or the mathematics that they attacked; it was the philosophical outlook they believed they detected in it. Some account of the chief philosophies of this time seems therefore to be necessary. Otherwise we shall fail to do justice to the issues raised by science and we shall see it rather more as Francis Bacon saw it: as something that ministers to the practical needs of men and extends the *imperium hominis,* the power of the human mind. Such a view ignores many important considerations. For the great watershed that the seventeenth century represents is that which divides essentially teleological and philosophical explanations from those which are deterministic and scientific. An enormous change is brought about when men cease to wonder why God arranges things as they are, and ask instead what laws operate in the causation of events. Philosophy can perhaps reconcile man to the universe in which he finds himself, but this is not a task to which scientific work ever addresses itself. In a scientific age it is assumed as a mark of the mature mind that human desires are not seen in any way to be a factor which will help to explain how the universe is what it is.

So radically has our thinking altered in the past three hundred years that Aristotle's philosophy of nature is not easy for us to grasp. Nor from Aristotle's own works can we be sure that we shall recover the ideas of the seventeenth-century Aristotelians, so accustomed were they to adapt their views so as to accommodate new discoveries when this was felt to be necessary. On the whole this seems to have been a rare occurrence, however. The merit of the Aristotelian philosophy was that it was complete and in a way science was precluded from disturbing it at all seriously.

For right from the beginning Aristotle used a special classification according to which there are sciences which aim at knowledge for its own sake, those which aim at knowledge as a guide to conduct, and those which make possible the production of something useful or beautiful. Physics and mathematics belong, with theology, to the first group, which consists of theoretical, not practical or productive, sciences, so that from the very start his treatment was unsuited to physics as we know it. According to Ross (*Aristotle,* Chapter 3) physics 'deals with things that have a separate existence but are not unchangeable', while mathematics deals with things that are 'unchangeable but have no separate existence'. No doubt Aristotle was much influenced here by his master Plato, who held that geometrical figures can only 'exist' in a realm of ideal 'Forms' and are only imperfectly realized on earth. Such figures, Aristotle held, cannot belong to matter, but only to pure extension. Thus form is, in Aristotle's philosophy, distinct from matter, for matter can be made to take various forms. Such an abstraction seems strange to us, but it is essential for the simplest understanding of Aristotelianism. For physics was primarily the study of the form of things. It is distinct, says Ross, 'from a study which concentrates entirely on matter, which reduces a living body for instance, or an inanimate chemical compound, to its elements'. It was certainly not a mathematical study and A. C. Crombie in his book *Augustine to Galileo* remarks that the problem of using mathematics in explaining the physical world 'remained, in fact, one of the central methodological problems, and was in many ways *the* central problem, of natural science down to the seventeenth century'.

Aristotle really created an impasse for physics by his theoretical separation of that study from mathematics. Yet this did not trouble him, since he took an entirely different view of natural phenomena from that which we are accustomed to take. To understand any change, according to his philosophy, we need to appreciate altogether four kinds of cause. There is first the *material* cause, which tells us the kind of matter from which a thing is made. Aristotle did not think of all matter as formless:

this was a question of degree, a bar of iron, for example, having a form which was not significant if the iron was to be wrought into something quite different. Secondly there was the *formal* cause which was the shape or pattern which it was sought to obtain. Aristotle could consider the form of a statue as being among the causes that produce it, but it was the intelligible structure of things that specially appealed to him. 'Form', says Ross, 'for Aristotle embraces a variety of meanings.' We certainly find seventeenth-century Aristotelians concerning themselves with the form of a movement, by which, presumably, they meant its intelligible shape, such as the curve traced out in for example a parabola or an ellipse.

It is the *efficient* cause that comes nearest to our view of causation, but here again Aristotle's view is not the same as ours because he can include a human agency, as well as an impersonal one, amongst those that operate. The efficient cause is 'that from which comes the immediate origin of the movement', but by itself this would not be sufficient to produce a certain effect. For when one circumstance necessarily leads to another Aristotle insisted that it is the conclusion that determines the result just as much as, and in general more than, the efficient cause. The conclusion, or the end that is sought, is Aristotle's fourth type of cause, his *final* cause. It is this that colours his whole philosophy, for in his view all the innate impulses to movement that exist in nature lead to the realization of the form which is proper to them. An acorn becomes, in time, an oak. To this end all is subservient. Form is by degrees imposed on matter and in the oak the final cause accomplishes itself. As we should express it the oak is the purpose or end which has been sought, and this form was potential within the acorn from the beginning. All change is ultimately the realization of what is potential and thus all nature is drawn onwards towards the ends which must be accomplished, consciously or unconsciously.

As Ross says 'Aristotle is in fact pronouncing in favour of teleology against mere mechanism'. Yet by leaving scope for the efficient cause his teleology is not completely opposed to determinism. For the seventeenth-century Aristotelians, however, the form of a motion was more important than the efficient cause at work. The curve could be studied, therefore, without any serious consideration of what we should call the forces at work. Thus the new physical science was subtly anti-Aristotelian in its methods let alone any results that might be seen in this light. The Aristotelians could perform experiments but their reasoning precluded the discovery of laws of scientific form. It is now well known that some Aristotelians were dissatisfied with received ideas, so that the scientific movement owes something to criticisms made within the system. Professor Butterfield in his *Origins of Modern Science* dwelt on this at length but his great satisfaction with the Aristotelians who performed experiments which argued against their predilections cannot obscure the fact that the Aristotelian system was assuredly most unsuited to the development of mathematical physics.

When we read about the Aristotelian system today the thing that must impress us is the loss of emotional satisfaction that we have suffered. For this system placed the earth at the centre of the universe and showed us unmistakably how there was a purpose in all the veriest details of our world. If it were not for the influence of the sun the four elements, earth, water, air and fire would range themselves in concentric spheres and all motion except that of the heavenly bodies would cease. The circular motions of these alone were necessary, but while the sun 'advances' and 'recedes', generation and decay will continue on the earth and there will be transmutation among the elements. Even so each element tends to find its proper place, water above earth, air above water and so forth. There is no sense, therefore, in asking why such things should happen. Empty space, the *void* of the atomists, appeared illogical to Aristotle, and he advanced many arguments to this end. The whole system he constructed was intensely logical. The universe formed an interconnected whole such that everything made sense from the Aristotelian point of view. The general structure of the universe must, indeed, be as it is. No strange discoveries such as spots on the sun could be taken seriously, therefore. In the sublunary sphere we are subject to incessant change, much of it perhaps perplexing and contrary to our desires. Yet we are reconciled by the reflection that the final causes inherent in the universe are being served. In the realm beyond the moon, not so very far away, the heavenly spheres could be imagined endlessly turning, the bodies belonging to them free from generation or decay. The heavens were, therefore, a realm of perfection on which men could gaze with a sense of completion.

Enough has been said to indicate the teleological nature of Aristotelian explanations. During the seventeenth century there was an attempt to accommodate the new discoveries, so far as appeared necessary, within the system. The brutal assertion that the system was wrong in fact and principle from beginning to end was one which could scarcely be considered. Even the most advanced Aristotelians shrank from such a calamity. Yet in the end this was the conclusion men reached.

It is in the pages of some of the works of the great Italian scientist Galileo that we find the most perceptive treatment of these philosophical differences. Galileo must be remembered as a great astronomer and experimentalist. He also deserves to be remembered in a way as a philosopher, the first, perhaps, to have seen and explained how the kind of explanation given by Aristotle could be overthrown by careful quantitative study. His book *Il Saggiatore* 'The Assayer' (dedicated to Pope Urban VIII) was really a landmark in the history of scientific thought, for there Galileo lays bare the requirements of mechanical explanations. This book dealt with some of the conceptions that were later to be employed in so masterly a way by Newton. Read in conjunction with passages from his *Dialogue Concerning the Two Chief Systems of the World* it certainly brings out the collision between different philosophical habits of mind. Galileo lived through an ordeal produced by this collision. As is well known, he had to appear before a solemn tribunal in Rome and read out a prepared statement condemning as heretical all the new work on the Copernican system. 'We arrogate too much to ourselves', he had written in his *Two Chief Systems,* 'when we assume that the care of us alone is the adequate and sufficient work and limit beyond which the Divine wisdom and power do nothing and dispose of nothing. I feel confident that nothing is omitted from God's providence which concerns the government of human affairs; but that there may not be other things in the universe dependent on His supreme power, I cannot, with what power of reasoning I possess, bring myself to believe.' Modest words, one would have said today, by no means lacking in religious feeling. But the new note which suggested a universe which went beyond the bounds of human need was one which was not considered prudent. The heretical monk Giordano Bruno had preached this new gospel in its most violent form and he had been burned at the stake.

The news of Galileo's condemnation by the Papal court had considerable effects all over Europe. There can be little doubt that it caused some writers to be more cautious in their statements, while on the other hand it gave encouragement to the critics of science amongst the Aristotelians. It was in this atmosphere of uncertainty, while there was still much force in the charge of heresy, that the philosopher Descartes developed his ideas until they formed, as it were, an alternative system. Great must have been the relief at the discovery that here there was a persuasive and scientific thinker whose explanations offered a compromise and did what the discredited Aristotelian system could do no longer, which was to provide a satisfactory relation between the claims of Copernicanism on the one hand and the inviolable claims of religious authority on the other.

There can be little doubt that Descartes (1596–1650) belongs in spirit to the modern age, and not to the Middle Ages which Aristotelianism represents. He was, to begin with, extremely critical of what passed for learning in the world in which he grew up. He was amazed at the failure of men to see the importance of mathematics, and develop it as he felt sure it could be developed. While acknowledging throughout his life certain debts to his teachers at the Jesuit College of La Flêche he ended by believing that nothing that was then taught was worth knowing. And he ended his account of his education with the famous words 'For these reasons, as soon as my age permitted me to pass from under the control of my instructors, I entirely abandoned the study of letters and resolved no longer to seek any other science than the knowledge of myself, or of the great book of the world'. If we get nothing else from Descartes's *Discourse on Method* we should get this sovereign notion, that the only education worth having is, in the end, that which we find for ourselves.

Although retiring and modest in nature Descartes lived by no means an inactive life. He came of a noble family and served in the army, first under Prince Maurice of Orange in the Low Countries during the heroic struggle with Spain, then he fought on the Austrian side at the Battle of White Hill near Prague. He was to have as his pupils the Princess Elizabeth, daughter of Frederick the Elector Palatine, and in his later years Queen Christina of Sweden. Early in life Descartes saw that the Copernican system could not stand by itself and needed, as he felt, a system of mechanics to explain it. This was a great perception. Unfortunately, when he heard of the condemnation of Galileo at Rome in 1633 for much the same point of view he abandoned work on his great book *Le Monde* which was published fourteen years after his death, in 1664. Descartes did not wish to fall foul of the Church. His mechanical ideas, dealt with in a more detached manner, appeared in his *Principia Philosophiae* of 1644.

It is clear now that a good deal of the excitement caused by science in the mid-seventeenth century was due to the Cartesian philosophy. Science, indeed, has never enlisted great popular support unless it has provided a new vision and this from time to time has happened. The mid-seventeenth century was such a time. In certain technicalities there had indeed been a long preparation for the *éclaircissement* which took place. A certain amount of experimental and mathematical work seems to owe its origin to the fertile imagination of Leonardo da Vinci, whose notebooks were copied and whose ideas reached men of a much later age. The works of Archimedes had a great vogue and both Benedetti (1530–90) and Simon Stevin (1548–1620) derived much from the great Greek thinker. Descartes travelled about a good deal. He knew a number of aristocratic and well-educated people such as Constantin Huygens, Secretary to Frederick Henry, Prince of Orange, and an excellent example of the culture of his time. His active imagination and fertile mathematical genius were both brought to bear on the great task of finding a new, rational, interpretation of nature which would be true where Aristotelianism had been found to be false. Yet, like Aristotelianism, this interpretation was concerned not so much with the separate, isolated, problems that could be studied with the help of experiments, but rather with great general ideas from which the lesser truths could be deduced.

It is very easy for the modern scientist to say that Descartes went wrong, whereas his contemporary Galileo found the right road. It fell to the Dutch scientist Christian Huygens to make almost a comparative study here and it was he who restored the tradition of Galileo and rejected the methods Descartes used in physics. But at the time Descartes seemed to many to have found the key and his system was discussed and taught all over Europe. Even in Cambridge, some years after the publication of Newton's monumental *Principia,* the Cartesian philosophy continued to be taught.

Descartes's method was not so much 'scientific' as 'intellectual'. And here he may have fallen into a trap prepared for him by his education. 'I think, therefore I am' was his starting-point. This represented the one conclusion from immediate experience Descartes said he could not reject. All else, when exposed to his method of doubt, seemed uncertain. He rejected the syllogism of Aristotle; instead the discoveries of reason lay, he believed, in the perception of the general in the particular. As a mathematician Descartes believed that many truths could be seen to be self-evident. Building on these, what recourse he had to experiment seems to have been perfunctory. The reason for this seems to be that, rather like Plato, he thought that only very imperfect impressions could be gained in this way. The real world was an intelligible world. This was his faith. He decided for example on general theoretical grounds that a vacuum could not exist. All space must therefore be full of some subtle matter that eludes the senses. Only thus could an event at one place influence another at a distant point. It seems clear that not only magnetism but gravity —and light—occurred to him as examples of phenomena which required space to be a plenum. The reason for this was that Descartes wished to explain all phenomena in mechanical terms. If the teleology of Aristotle were given up men needed a new guiding principle and Descartes, in an extraordinary effort of imagination, showed how this could be found in his mechanical theories. His system had, too, the merit that it gave due place to natural laws and his one misfortune was that he did not succeed, with his mathematical-intuitional method, in formulating them correctly. What he did was to inspire a generation with a vision of Nature as a sphere of universal law embracing planetary motion, rainbows, the properties of magnets and of lenses—all of which could be explained by reference to the underlying mechanism. There seemed no limit to the field of scientific investigation. The explanations given by Descartes possessed an admirable economy of principles. What he chiefly seemed to have demonstrated was that the mechanical processes occurring in nature are such that they can be readily comprehended by the human reason. The discovery that the world was rational was just as exciting as the old belief that it exhibited moral purposes. Indeed it was a good deal more exciting. It certainly suited a mentality that was enlarged by geographical exploration, stimulated by new sources of wealth and power, and accustomed to a greater degree of organization and planning in human affairs than had been known in the past.

It was the view of a great eighteenth-century mathematician that: 'le grand mérite de Descartes est d'avoir vu que le problème du monde est un problème de mécanique.' In his so-called vortex theory the sun is the centre of a vast rotating quantity of 'subtle matter', that is, matter that we do not ordinarily perceive or detect. This matter, according to Descartes, keeps the planets moving in their orbits. They certainly all move in the same sense and very nearly in the same plane. The earth rotates on its axis in the same direction as the moon goes round the earth. Jupiter rotates, also, in the same direction as its satellites go round. 'It might therefore be supposed', wrote an eighteenth-century commentator, 'that if the whole planetary region were filled with a fluid matter, the sun, by turning round on its own axis, might communicate motion first to that part of the fluid which is contiguous, and by degrees propagate the like motion to the parts more remote. After the same manner, the earth might communicate motion to this fluid, to a distance sufficient to carry round the moon, and Jupiter communicates the like to the distance of its satellites.' There was more to the vortex theory than this, for Descartes used the subtle matter to explain the transmission of light, the action of gravity towards the centre of the earth, magnetic forces, and other phenomena. He was completely opposed to the notion that there could be empty space and he also rejected the atomic theory, coming into conflict here with the philosopher Gassendi whose own system united Epicureanism and the ideas of Galileo.

The problem of gravity exercised many men in the first half of the seventeenth century and although Newton gave the first quantitative treatment he was by no means the inventor of the idea of a gravitational force acting across space. For William Gilbert, the physician to Queen Elizabeth, motion under gravity was 'a substantial form, special and particular, belonging to the primary bodies', words which indicate a more or less Aristotelian point of view. Kepler knew about Gilbert's study of magnetism and he considered gravity to be 'a mutual attraction between parent bodies which tend to unite and join together'. Why then, asked many men of science, do the earth and moon not become attracted so that they come together? What keeps the moon up? This, as we know, is an incorrect form of the question. It led some to conclude that the bodies are kept *apart* by fluid pressure. The philosopher Roberval maintained, however, that gravity is a mutual attraction between the particles of bodies and stated that he held this view as early as 1636. In 1646 Descartes certainly ridiculed this 'absurd notion' of Roberval. It would mean, he thought, that a particle of matter must be endowed with consciousness so that it could know what happened across space and could in some occult manner exert its influence there. Descartes's philosophy attributed to matter the quality of being extended in space, and to the mind the quality of knowing. He had, therefore, the *res extensa* and the *res cogitans* as the foundation of his analysis. Such ideas as Roberval's were to him nothing but a confusion. Even Huygens followed Descartes in seeking to reduce gravity to some effect in fluid mechanics. As early as about 1659 Huygens realized that a force towards the centre is needed to keep a body moving in a circle and he worked out how this varied with the speed and the radius. But because of his philosophical outlook he did not see the possibility of uniting the idea of gravitational attraction with that of centrifugal force as did, later, Halley and Newton.

In all his work Descartes supposed that motion can only be

transferred from one body to another by direct or indirect impact. His assumption was that the total amount of motion in the world is constant. There was the germ of a useful idea here but 'motion' is not a satisfactory conception. Descartes tried to make things better by distinguishing between the speed of a body and its 'determination' or direction, but he never pushed his analysis to a satisfactory conclusion. Galileo, Huygens and Newton are the true founders of mechanics. Descartes appears to have known that experiments did not accord with his theories: he thought that his own theories were correct and that in the experiments the necessary conditions could not be realized! This is an interesting example of the triumph of expectation over observation. Descartes' position in the history of science is certainly equivocal. As a mathematician and philosopher he merits our admiration. One wonders, as one looks at his portrait in the Louvre, whether he would have cared about our rather low estimate of him as a man of science. His expression, as Frans Hals caught it, seems to suggest that he would have been unmoved.

By the end of the seventeenth century warfare amongst the philosophies had by no means come to an end. Newton seems to have remained uncertain about the final constituents of the universe and whether, for example, there may be a luminiferous ether. There was a succession of philosophers who belonged to the Cartesian school, but only one of them, whose affinities with Descartes are slight, deserves immortal fame, and this was the philosopher Spinoza. With Spinoza (1632–77) philosophy severed the ties that linked it with natural science. Although he began by studying Descartes and attempted to give his *Ethics* the appearance of mathematical demonstration Spinoza was neither a mathematician nor a scientist and an exposition of his views lies outside the range of this book. There is, however, running through his writings a conception which is closely akin to the new convictions that dawned on others besides himself at this period: the conception of natural law. In Spinoza's philosophy the world and all beings in it are seen as from the loftiest height and a kind of impersonality belongs to all his descriptions. Good and evil are, for example, relative terms, for they apply in truth to what are simply events. Yet events happen as a result of laws which belong one might almost say to the mentality of the world. Avoiding Descartes's dualism of mind and matter Spinoza taught that these are one but that they can be considered in the light of their special attributes. There was no real difference for him between mind as represented by God and matter as represented by Nature. In something of a Cartesian manner he saw the connexions between things as essentially the same as the connexion between ideas, but the aim of his philosophy was not to give an account of physical phenomena.

It seems clear that Spinoza attempted to solve certain profound questions which arise in Descartes's dualistic philosophy. And his solution consisted in abandoning the dualism of mind and matter and attempting to treat them as modes of one reality which he termed 'substance'. In Spinoza's *Ethics* we find a great attempt to rehabilitate man in a world from which he was divorced with the advent of the deterministic laws of science. But the solution Spinoza proposed seemed austere and bleak. The extreme detachment of mind proper in mathematics and physics seemed iniquitous and blasphemous when it was manifested in ethics and metaphysics. Not for a long time were his writings admired or their religious qualities acknowledged.

Descartes was not truly scientific in his outlook, since he repeated some of the errors of Aristotle through deciding in advance what form explanations should take. Taking extension and motion to be the primary attributes of matter he set himself an impossible task in constructing a sound theory. 'Give me extension and motion and I will construct the world,' he boldly declared in *Le Monde* but in fact he failed to do justice to quite simple phenomena such as the results of collisions between two billiard balls. The philosophy of Spinoza was even more than that of Descartes an expression of the tendency of modern thought to rely on itself unaided by authorities of any kind. It also shows, says Wolf (*History of Science and Technology*, sixteenth and seventeenth centuries), 'the new and friendly attitude towards Nature, and the growing suspicion of the need of the supernatural'. The article referred to in this book is one of the best short accounts of Spinoza's difficult philosophy that are to be found. At the end of the century a further attempt was made, this time by the German philosopher and mathematician Leibnitz, 'to vindicate' as Wolf expresses it, 'the reality and significance of the spiritual, and especially of finite spirits or souls, in the universe'.

Science, as we shall see, seemed to be calling into prominence a new and frightening philosophy which gave validity only to atoms, or lumps of matter possessing momentum or energy. The scientific analysis was later to require radiations, electrons, quanta and all the rest of our modern physical terminology. But the essence of the problem was perceived in the late seventeenth century by one or two isolated thinkers. Descartes is usually reckoned to be the father of modern philosophy because the relation of mind and matter has up to very recent times been one of the chief, if not the chief, problems he bequeathed to the modern age. But Leibnitz in Germany, Henry More, Isaac Barrow and Newton in England all showed in various ways a sense of uneasiness at the mechanistic trend of science. This trend can be found in the ancient atomic doctrines of ancient Greece although the modern notion of a scientific law of nature was needed to give it force. And laws of nature would have remained unknown without the enormous outburst of experiment and observation which is needed to establish them. That the laws are mathematically simple was at first a faith; but the exact form of the laws could not in most instances be discovered without experiment. It is therefore to the experimental activities of the seventeenth century that we must now turn.

CHAPTER FOUR

The Experimentalists

THE carrying out of simple experiments did not begin in the seventeenth century: it is on the contrary an ancient tradition which goes back to the Greeks. It persisted despite the suspicion in which experiments were held in Christendom up to the time of Galileo, after whom a great burst of experimental activity took place. What we have to consider in this short survey is not experiment as such, but the union of experiment with a satisfactory scientific method.

The great mathematician Archimedes of Syracuse (287–217 B.C.) is for our purpose easily the most impressive of the ancient Greek philosophers, for he practically anticipated the ideas on scientific method that the seventeenth century established. Archimedes' work on the law of the lever, on centres of gravity and on hydrostatics all show that he must have carried out many experiments. He does not describe them, however, any more than he gives his original methods in his mathematical works, for here too he seems to have relied on practical experiments to some degree. Nothing offers a better correction of the methods and outlook of Aristotle than a study of the work of Archimedes. 'Among ancient mathematicians', says Crombie, 'Archimedes had been the most successful in combining mathematics with experimental inquiry; because of this he became the ideal of the sixteenth century. His method was to select definite and limited problems. He then formulated hypotheses which he either regarded, in the Euclidean manner, as self-evident axioms or could verify by simple experiments. The consequences of these he then deduced and experimentally verified.' It was for these reasons that, when a translation of some of his work became available through the productions of the printing presses, his influence became very great. Both Galileo and Huygens, two giants amongst the experimentalists, were influenced by him.

We have to remember that much of Greek thought perished

in the downfall of their civilization. Archimedes himself was slain by a Roman soldier, Marcellus, story has it while he was engaged in a mathematical study. In Alexandria, during the third and second centuries B.C. it seems likely that a good deal of experimental work of a sort took place. A number of mechanical inventions date from these times, some of them being associated with the obscure figure of Hero (second century B.C.) whose book records a number of devices which could be made to work with compressed air or steam. All this work was lost from sight for centuries. After the translation of some of Aristotle's works from an Arabic edition in the twelfth and thirteenth centuries we can trace the work of a new school of thinkers in Europe, including Jordanus Nemorarius (thirteenth century) who advanced mechanics in one or two respects. Only minor works of Archimedes were known and his influence is hard to estimate until the sixteenth century. Leonardo da Vinci we know studied him; but the real, the significant interest of Archimedes is that his work, across two thousand years, provided an important starting-point for both Galileo and Huygens.

For the remarkable thing is that for centuries nearly all the experimenting that there was had been abortive. When experiment was guided by a thoroughly erroneous philosophy, when above all it was purely qualitative and not concerned to *measure,* experiment contributed very little to the advance of science. We have a good example of this in the pursuit of alchemy from Alexandrian times (say second century B.C.) down to the seventeenth century. During this time it is impossible to reckon the thousands of experiments that must have been performed. Yet they had hardly any significant results. The trouble was that the alchemists were guided by Aristotelian or neo-Platonic ideas which led them hopelessly astray. The attempt, for example, to get some kind of featureless matter and then bestow upon it all the required qualities of gold can be seen as a practical application of a general philosophy. But it was, of course, fruitless. Yet through the centuries the attempts to carry out transmutation went on, and alchemy became more and more irrational and decadent. So that we have the curious result that in the seventeenth century alchemy was at its lowest point, being riddled with occult beliefs akin to those found in astrology, while at the same time men like van Helmont, Boyle, Hooke and Rey had begun a truly empirical study which was to provide the foundation of chemistry. The introduction of mathematics into science called, of course, for better education and a clearer, more rational, mentality. By itself mathematics was inadequate: Descartes is the best example of this fact. It was when mathematics and experiment were brought together in a reciprocal relationship that the new method of the physical sciences was created.

It is interesting to reflect on the advantages to science of its support at first by aristocratic amateurs. In the seventeenth century the advantages of aristocratic education and circumstances still weighed quite heavily. This is less evident in the second half of the century. It seems clear that Francis Bacon's writings were partly responsible for this aristocratic interest. William Gilbert (1540–1603), physician to Queen Elizabeth, sought to follow Bacon's principles. His experiments on magnets and electrified bodies aroused widespread interest. Experiment continued to be fashionable at court both in England and France, and Descartes's fascinating theories made science seem relatively easy and diverting. It was not long, however, before all studies became more technical and to this extent repellent to the dilettante. Something like professional zeal was then needed.

Aristocratic example was important, however, in securing freedom from the charge of black art and necromancy. This attitude towards experiment seems to have been partly superstitious, because of the fear of terrible consequences of traffic with evil powers, and partly rational because the philosophical tradition was intellectual and not concerned with the practical arts. In 1560 an *Accademia Secretorum Naturae* existed for a brief time in Naples, but the Pope had it closed because of suspicion of black arts. Then in 1603 came the *Accademia dei Lincei* but this again was not permanent. It was the *Accademia del Cimento* founded in Florence in 1657 by some followers of Galileo which first achieved renown for its experimental inquiries. This society had the support of the Duke of Tuscany but this could not protect it altogether against the suspicions of the Inquisition. It broke up, and two of its members made their way to Paris where there were groups associated with Mersenne and Gassendi, both Catholic priests of liberal outlook.

Meanwhile in London, and later in Oxford, there was about this time an 'experimental Philosophicall clubbe' which was active even in the midst of the Civil War. This society became re-established in London in 1660 and in 1662 was granted a royal charter and incorporated as the Royal Society. Louis XIV, following the advice of his minister Colbert, supported with his patronage a similar society, the *Académie Royale des Sciences* founded in 1666. Both Bacon and Descartes had urged the importance of co-operation amongst experimentalists. 'The principal occupation of this assembly', wrote Huygens of the *Académie Royale* he did so much to found, 'must be the practical study of natural history following the plan of Verulam [Bacon]. This subject consists of experiments and observations and is the only way to arrive at knowledge of the causes of all that one sees in Nature. . . .'

It is probably no accident that in England experimental science at first found most of its supporters on the Royalist side and not among the Puritans. Cromwell's party was concerned essentially with political and religious questions and might not seem to have been opposed to science. Yet the religious side of the movement was in some aspects an archaic continuation of the Reformation—it looked back not forward. The Roundheads were less sympathetic to free inquiry than were the Royalists, and they were active in witch hunting, something which had long been in decline (cf. Lecky, *Rise of Rationalism*). The dates of the English Royal Society which have been given can be considered therefore alongside the dates of the dictatorship and of the restoration of the monarchy.

We must not underestimate the place of chemistry in the studies of the English amateurs. As early as June 1654 the prolific writer and student of chemistry, Robert Boyle, was settled in Oxford and here worked for a time his equally famous assistant Robert Hooke. Boyle introduced Peter Sthael to give for the first time a course of lectures on chemistry at Oxford. His lectures aroused much interest and the philosopher John Locke was among those who attended them. Chemistry continued, however, to be a backward subject and one frank student 'confessed that he had learnt nothing in his whole life-time, which he devoted to chemistry, except that he knew nothing of it'. The problems examined by members of these societies were varied and for a long time lacked co-ordination. Sprat's *History of the Royal Society* gives some indication of the work done in the early years. The experiments he mentioned fell into groups: there were those which concerned fire and flame, the nature and uses of air, the properties of water; there were also experiments concerned with ores and metals, with vegetables, medical and anatomical experiments, experiments on freezing and expansion and certain other properties of matter, experiments on sound and light, and finally experiments on motion (mechanics) and the force of gravity. Listed in this way Sprat's account of the experiments gives an impression of more careful planning than in fact took place. Many of the experiments were really the outcome of lively curiosity, like the ones he mentions 'of destroying *Mites* by several Fumes; of the equivocal Generation of *Insects*; of feeding a *Carp* in the Air; of making Insects with Cheese, and Sack; of killing Water-Newts, Toads, and Sloworms with several Salts; of killing Frogs, by touching the Skin with Vinegar, Pitch or Mercury; of a Spider's not being inchanted by a Circle of *Unicorns Horn,* or *Irish Earth,* laid round about it'. Others, on the other hand, were more in accord with the tradition of Galileo: '*Experiments* of the Swiftness of a Bullet shot with extraordinary Power; of the best Figure of the Weight of a *Pendulum* for *Motion*; of the Motion of pendulous Bodies of various Figures; to determine the Length of *Pendulums,* to find the Velocity of the Vibrations of a sounding String; to find the Velocity of *Motion,* propagated by a very long extended Wire; for explaining the Inflection of a strait Motion into a circular, by a supervening attractive Power towards the Center, in order to the explaining of the *Motion* of the Planets.'

In London there were Boyle, Hooke, Wren, Halley, Lord Brouncker the first President of the Royal Society, Wilkins, Goddard, John Evelyn, the indefatigable secretary Henry Oldenburg and several others. Christopher Wren, Hooke and Halley joined the Society shortly after its foundation and gradually the support of non-scientists became less important. But both the Paris and London societies attracted a number of men who were interested but never actively engaged in science. At Paris there were at first Huygens, the mathematician Roberval, the astronomers Auzout and Buot, the king's librarian Carcavy, and a few others including Frenicle de Bessy. These were joined by Cassini and Jean Picard, both fine astronomers, the student of mechanics Mariotte and one or two engineers and civil servants like Pierre Petit. It was an able group with many of the earlier Cartesians apparently deliberately excluded.

To some extent the study of science in these new societies was stimulated by practical needs of the times; to some extent it was the result of intellectual curiosity which now felt itself free. There is no difficulty in tracing utilitarian aims in seventeenth-century science. In those days there were great difficulties and dangers in navigating ships on long voyages. England, Holland and France were coming to depend more and more on foreign trade, and valuable cargoes had to be hazarded through unreliable means of navigation. Great sums stood to be saved by the discovery of a practical means of finding a ship's longitude at sea, and in pursuing a solution to this problem men of science paid special attention to astronomy and the construction of a suitable chronometer. For some time it was thought that the periodic eclipses of Jupiter's satellites could be used as a sort of celestial clock from which standard time could be obtained. The idea was sound in theory but useless in practice. It is impossible to use an astronomical telescope if there is vibration or movement of its support and in any case the uncertainty of the weather made the method unsuitable. The problem was not solved until the eighteenth century although Huygens continued to experiment with marine clocks all his life.

This is just one illustration of the relationship between commerce and science. But the practical aspect of science, while it gave rise to many interesting experiments, was never a complete explanation of seventeenth-century enthusiasm. The great book of Nature lay open to be read, and as they sought to understand it many of the men of science, Robert Boyle especially, felt a religious duty in what they were doing. 'I had rather believe all the fables in the "Legend" and the "Talmud" and the "Alcoran",' wrote Francis Bacon, 'than that this universal frame is without a mind. And, therefore, God never wrought miracle to convince atheism, because His ordinary works convince it.' This point of view seems to have been quite common in Protestant England. Bishop Ward and Bishop Wilkins, a great student of Campanella, both hoped for great things from science, and Bishop Sprat summed up their outlook when he said that the experimentalists had always before their eyes 'the Beauty, Wonder and Contrivance of God's works'.

In Paris it was rather different. There a fashionable atheism, or at least a form of Stoicism, was prevalent and Huygens, the dominant figure of his time, quite unlike Boyle, showed a certain remoteness from the beliefs of either Catholic or Calvinist churches. Perhaps the situation was partly the consequence of the reactionary writings of the Jesuits— men like Père Fabri, Père Mousnier and the Abbé Catelan, all of whom used their energies to defend Aristotelian doctrines and belittle nearly all new discoveries. Some of them took a stand on the newly accepted writings of Descartes. For Descartes's writings had a curious reception. At first uniformly opposed, the same thing happened to them as had long ago happened to the writings of Aristotle: they became authoritative and to attack them was more or less heretical. Protestantism, by exchanging the infallible Church for the infallible Book, never extended dogmatic teaching over the whole field of learning.

Yet in England there was by no means complete toleration for any general philosophical theory. The experiences of Thomas Hobbes illustrate this. The writer of *Leviathan* is now regarded as a prophetic thinker. Like his contemporary Spinoza, Hobbes was much execrated in his lifetime and is now much admired. Hobbes, like Spinoza, was suspected of atheism. His interest for the historian of science lies chiefly in his materialistic philosophy. Like many philosophical materialists Hobbes belonged to a class which was influenced by science and yet had neither scientific training nor any real sympathy with the true aims of science. Few at that time, for example, would agree with Hobbes in trying to reduce all the activities of living creatures to the interplay of physical forces. Man for him was only an animal plus an intellectual faculty, and all men's motives resulted from fear and the desire for power. The physical world for him was simply a realm of determinism—the sort of world, almost, that the Epicureans had depicted, with their whirling concourses of atoms. Religion consequently was for Hobbes 'not philosophy but law'. The men of science in England were embarrassed by the charge that they were 'Hobbists', for they liked Hobbes with his presumptuous claims to be a mathematician and his scorn for experiments little better than the churchmen liked his atheism.

In the seventeenth century the universe began to appear far vaster and far less comprehensible than Galileo or Descartes would ever have imagined. Before Newton's *Principia* appeared and men were confronted with the task of assimilating all that it contained, the scientific societies had accumulated important data. In 1670–72, for example, there was as has been mentioned an important expedition sent out from Paris to Cayenne. The chief aim was to make observations both at Cayenne and at Paris, mainly on the planet Mars, from which the first reliable estimate of the size of the solar system could be deduced. The principle employed was that of a triangulation survey of a part of the earth, giving a base line in terms of which the distance of the planet could be calculated from simultaneous determinations of its altitude. It was estimated that the sun is distant from the earth some eighty-seven million miles. From this the least distance of the nearest stars could be estimated very approximately. Compared with the figure of some five million miles accepted by the astronomer Ptolemy the new figures were very surprising. The universe, it seemed, proved to be more surprising the more it was studied—a feeling expressed by Fontenelle when he lightly remarked: 'The Fixed Stars cannot be less distant from the Earth, than twenty-seven thousand, six hundred and fifty times the distance from hence to the Sun, which is thirty-three millions of leagues, and if you displease an astronomer, he will place them yet farther off.'

Thus before the time of Newton science was already exerting an influence in the world of thought, chiefly as a result of new discoveries. Many of the discoveries were by no means spectacular but had their effect when theoretical advances followed. The history of science is full of examples of the way in which knowledge of a remote and technical nature can lead in time to conclusions which are profoundly important for ordinary man; even before the time of Newton this was becoming clear. Copernicus's theory could for a time be regarded as chiefly a convenience for astronomers but the development of the telescope greatly strengthened the argument in its favour. The discovery of the phases of Venus and later the observation of the rotation of Jupiter placed the theory in an unassailable position and thus made the motion of the Earth a fact which was no longer disputable. By the end of the century there was much speculation whether other planets besides the Earth are inhabited. Such notions were quite contrary to Scripture and made for scepticism in religion.

After 1650 English readers could enjoy Galileo's long debate entitled *Dialogue on the Two Chief Systems of the World* in Salusbury's translation. Galileo died in 1642 but the delayed action caused by the work of this great Italian astronomer and experimentalist was very great. By the mid-century copies of his *Two Chief Systems,* and his later more technical treatise on mechanics, *Dialogue concerning Two New Sciences* were being read all over Europe, and men were taking to heart the view expressed by Galileo that in experimental science we have to do with an approach to truth which owes nothing to authority or human preference. 'If this which we dispute', says Salviati, 'were some point of Law, or other part of the Studies called *Humanity,* wherein there is neither truth nor falsehood, if we will give sufficient credit to the acuteness of the wit, readiness of answers, and the general practice of Writers, then he who most aboundeth in these, makes his reason more probable and plausible; but in Natural Sciences, the conclusions of which are true and necessary, and wherewith the judgments of men have nothing to do, one is to be more cautious how he goeth about to maintain anything that is false; for a man but of an ordinary wit, if it be his good fortune to be of the right side, may lay a thousand *Demosthenes* and a thousand *Aristotles* at his feet.'

The Two Chief Systems was not, however, the last book Galileo wrote. It is indeed of much less technical importance than his *Dialogues Concerning Two New Sciences* which he wrote at Arcetri after his condemnation. The manuscript was sent secretly to Amsterdam and the book was published in 1638 by the famous

Elzevir's press. The two sciences of which Galileo wrote were the strength of materials and the study of accelerated motion. These subjects were treated in the form of a discussion once more between Salviati, Sagredo and Simplicio who were the characters in his earlier book. It is, however, a very different work from the *Two Chief Systems,* and Galileo himself thought it 'superior to everything else of mine hitherto published'. It contained the results of more than thirty years' work, covering indeed almost the whole of his work in mechanics; and it carried physical science forward a very great stride.

Before going on to give passages from these and other seventeenth-century works it seems necessary to remark that we are about to encounter a new and rather difficult kind of literature. Effort is needed to grasp what is being said, and the distance from the original inquiry to the end of the processes of reasoning may well seem very great. This is characteristic of scientific work. The effort to read Galileo, or Huygens, or Newton is worth while, and in this little essay the passages included are not excessively long. Nevertheless, some of the pages which follow may prove a little arid, and imagination is needed to grasp the quality of the investigation. This imagination should be well within the powers of the modern reader. In any case we are concerned here only with a few examples of scientific work. They take us on to a consideration of the work of Newton and beyond that point technicalities need not be treated in so great detail.

In the early seventeenth century the most important and at the same time controversial matters were those concerned with the existence of a vacuum and the rate of fall of heavy bodies. The latter subject had been badly muddled by Aristotle, and Galileo proceeded to disentangle the various true and false ideas about weight and vertical acceleration. Introducing a careful study he had made of the vibrations of pendulums, Galileo, through his spokesman Salviati, explains how it occurred to him to use the pendulum as a means of comparing the rate of fall of heavy and light bodies. Since the mass of a pendulum bob does not affect the time of swing it is clear that heavy and light bodies fall at the same rate. Then he goes on: 'As to the time of vibration of bodies suspended by threads of different lengths, they bear to each other the same proportion as the square roots of the lengths of the thread. . . .' The underlying law of natural acceleration under gravity Galileo finally discovered 'after repeated efforts'. But he was, as he says, 'led, by the hand as it were, in following the habit and custom of nature herself, in all her various other processes to employ only those means which are most common, simple and easy.' The laws of nature are, he believes, *simple* in their mathematical form and they can consequently be discovered by experiments. It is really remarkable how much Galileo discovered with the very simple means at his disposal. Quite clearly it was an easy matter for him, once the law of natural acceleration was known, to deduce all sorts of useful theorems. Thus he proved that the path of a projectile is a parabola, getting his result by considering the horizontal and vertical components of the velocity at any instant. He proved also that the times taken by a body falling along inclined planes which are chords of the same circle, and ending at the lowest point, are all equal. The greatest advance of all, however, was to make a distinction between what we call the mass and the weight of a body, and to lay it down as a law of nature that a force *accelerates* a body and is not required to keep it in motion (in a straight line with constant speed). It is inconceivable that even Newton's genius could have dispensed with this profoundly important preliminary study of the simple facts of force, mass, and acceleration. Moreover we must credit Galileo with the development of what is in effect an entirely new method. Experiment was employed by him with a far more clear understanding of what it could show than by any previous scientist. His method was in fact a mathematical and experimental one. He saw how important it was to make one quantity vary so as to trace concomitant variations in another, or how to eliminate disturbing factors which would otherwise obscure the real facts.

A quotation from the *Two New Sciences* will illustrate these points. We might for example take this study of the simple pendulum, in the course of which Galileo showed himself so fertile in ideas that the simplest facts begin to look significant and important. 'Let us see', says Salviati, 'whether we cannot derive from the pendulum a satisfactory solution of all these difficulties. And first, as to the question whether one and the same pendulum really performs its vibrations, large, medium, and small, all in exactly the same time, I shall rely upon what I have already heard from our Academician. He has clearly shown that the time of descent is the same along all chords, whatever the arcs which subtend them, as well along an arc of 180° (i.e. the whole diameter) as along one of 100°, 60°, 10°, 2°, $\frac{1}{2}$°, or 4′. It is understood, of course, that these arcs all terminate at the lowest point of the circle, where it touches the horizontal plane.

'If now we consider descent along arcs instead of their chords then, provided these do not exceed 90°, experiment shows that they are all traversed in equal times; but these times are greater for the chord than for the arc, an effect which is all the more remarkable because at first glance one would think just the opposite to be true. For since the terminal points of the two motions are the same and since the straight line included between these two points is the shortest distance between them, it would seem reasonable that motion along this line should be executed in the shortest time; but this is not the case, for the shortest time—and therefore the most rapid motion—is that employed along the arc of which this straight line is the chord.'

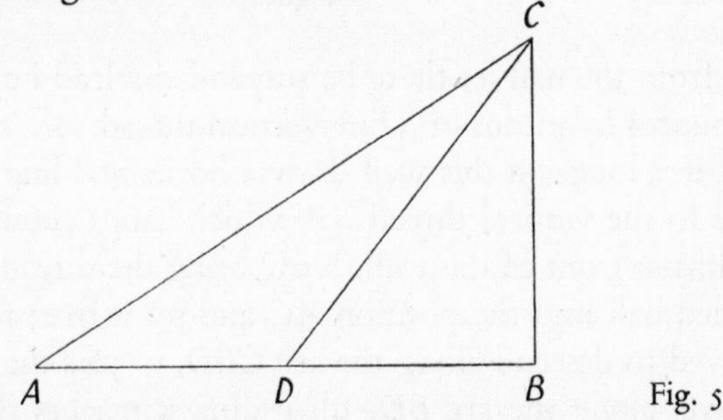

Fig. 5

Later on Salviati comes to the question of the speed which a body acquires in moving down a smooth inclined plane, for this obviously depends in some way on the slope of the plane and its length. In fact, there is a very simple law here: 'The speeds acquired by one and the same body moving down planes of different inclinations are equal when the heights of these planes are equal.' This means that a body will move under gravity from rest, through the distances *CA, CD* or *CB* in such a way that the speed at *A, D* or *B* is the same (Fig. 5.)

Now in Galileo's day the timing involved in such an experiment could not be done with sufficient accuracy. He therefore invents another experiment which makes the conclusion more certain. 'Imagine this page to represent a vertical wall,' says Salviati, 'with a nail driven into it.' And the diagram shown in Fig. 6 is then presented. Salviati goes on:

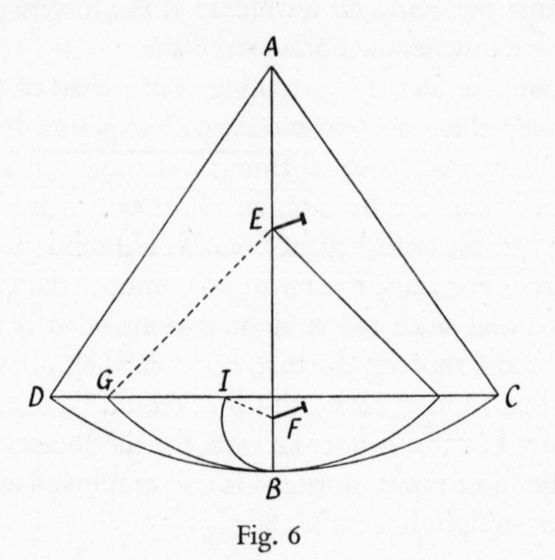

Fig. 6

'And from the nail let there be suspended a lead bullet of one or two ounces by means of a fine vertical thread, *AB,* say from four to six feet long, on this wall draw a horizontal line *DC,* at right angles to the vertical thread *AB,* which hangs about two finger-breadths in front of the wall. Now bring the thread *AB* with the attached ball into the position *AC* and set it free; first it will be observed to descend along the arc *CBD,* to pass the point *B,* and to travel along the arc *BD,* till it almost reaches the horizontal *CD,* a slight shortage being caused by the resistance of the air and the string; from this we may rightly infer that the ball in its descent through the arc *CB* acquired a momentum (*impeto*) on reaching *B,* which was just sufficient to carry it through a similar arc *BD* to the same height. Having repeated this experiment many times, let us now drive a nail into the wall close to the perpendicular *AB,* say at *E* or *F,* so that it projects out some five or six finger-breadths in order that the thread, again carrying the bullet through the arc *CB,* may strike upon the nail *E* when the bullet reaches *B*, and thus compel it to traverse the arc *BG*, described about *E* as centre. From this we can see what can be done by the same momentum (*impeto*) which previously starting at the same point *B* carried the same body through the arc *BD* to the horizontal *CD*. Now, gentlemen, you will observe with pleasure that the ball swings to the point *G* in the horizontal, and you would see the same thing happen if the obstacle were placed at some lower point, say at *F*, about which the ball would describe the arc *BI*, the rise of the ball always terminating exactly on the line *CD*. But when the nail is placed so low that the remainder of the thread below it will not reach to the height *CD* (which would happen if the nail were placed nearer *B* than to the intersection of *AB* with the horizontal *CD*) then the thread leaps over the nail and twists itself about it.

'This experiment leaves no room for doubt as to the truth of our supposition; for since the two arcs *CB* and *DB* are equal and similarly placed, the momentum (*momento*) acquired by the fall through the arc *CB* is the same as that gained by fall through the arc *BD*; therefore, the momentum acquired in the fall *BD* is equal to that which lifts the same body through the same arc from *B* to *D*; so, in general, every momentum acquired by fall through an arc is equal to that which can lift the same body through the same arc. But all these momenta (*momenti*) which cause a rise through the arcs *BD, BG,* and *BI* are equal, since they are produced by the same momentum, gained by fall through *CB,* as experiment shows. Therefore all the momenta gained by fall through the arcs *DB, GB, IB* are equal.'

This passage illustrates quite clearly the character of the book. The whole work is like this, partly experimental, partly mathematical and Galileo no sooner arrives at a general relationship of a mathematical sort than he deduces all sorts of particular cases of an interesting kind. In this way, by a succession of propositions and theorems he builds up his book in a way resembling Euclid's books of geometry. Huygens's *Horologium Oscillatorium* and Newton's *Principia* follow this pattern.

From about this time the continuity of the studies of mechanics seemed to be assured. The experiments given by Galileo were repeated and some of the problems left unsolved were felt to be so important that experiments on them could be found going on in several centres. In 1668 several experimentalists (Wallis, Wren, Huygens) published their conclusions on the subject of 'momentum'. This was a quantity which appeared to belong to a body in motion. In the so-called ballistic pendulum a hard wooden sphere on the end of a long string is allowed to swing, like a pendulum, so that it collides with another stationary pendulum (Fig. 7).

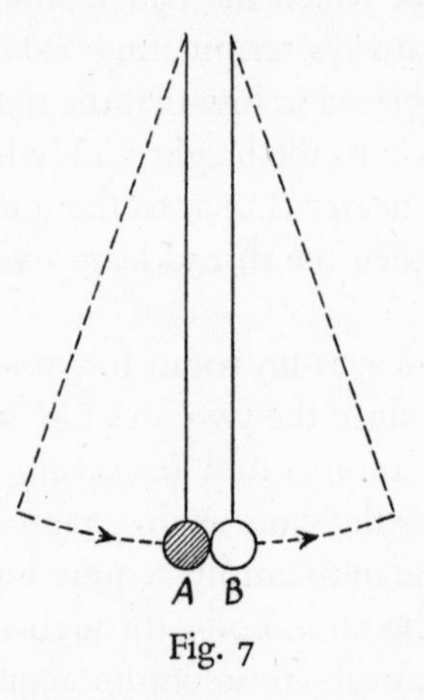

Fig. 7

The question is, if we know the masses of *A* and *B* how high will *B* ascend, and what will happen to *A*—will it rebound or come to rest, or continue some part of its motion. Intense interest was concentrated on this problem about 1660–70.

In case we should be tempted to dismiss such studies as trivial we should remember that *momentum* and *weight* provide two alternative approaches to the comparison of the masses of two bodies. Experiment showed that either method could be used and later on, in Newton's *Principia,* the equivalence of mass determined by momentum and by weight is taken for granted. To inquire why the two measures can be treated in this way is to raise some profound problems which are not dealt with in physics until we come to the work of Einstein.

The treatise on the theory of measuring time by means of the cycloidal pendulum, *Horologium Oscillatorium,* by Huygens showed an advance, in 1673, on anything published by Galileo. The chief discoveries of Huygens in mechanics may be mentioned at this point. The correct treatment of problems of momentum was worked out from 1652 onwards; Huygens made use of the product mv and also, in certain cases, of the quantity mv^2. He discovered a particularly important theorem in the course of his ballistic pendulum experiments, which was that the centre of gravity of a system of bodies cannot rise as a consequence of any movements of the bodies under gravity. This led him to a discovery of a special case of the law of conservation of energy. The word *energy* was not used but all the appropriate calculations were carried out. Much of this work is found in the *Horologium Oscillatorium* of 1673 in which Huygens solved the great problem set him as a young man by Mersenne: the problem of calculating the 'centre of oscillation' of a compound pendulum. This was much the hardest dynamical problem yet tackled by anyone.

It needs to be explained that any rigid body, which is arranged so that it can oscillate about an axis passing through it, is a 'compound pendulum'. A long uniform bar, pivoted at one end, or at a point along its length, is a compound pendulum. A bar carrying a massive bob at its lower end is the common sort of pendulum used in pendulum clocks. Here the distribution of masses is more complicated. The question which interested Huygens can be expressed thus: 'Given the shape of a compound pendulum can the period of its swing about a given axis be worked out by mathematics?' Huygens was more interested in this problem for a long time than he was in another problem he also studied with success: the magnitude of the 'centrifugal force' which is required to keep a body moving in a circle at constant speed.

This question of centrifugal force was to prove very important in the work of Newton on the rotation of the earth and the motion of planets. As is well known it was supposed by the Cartesians that the circular motion of the planets resulted from the movement in a 'vortex' of an invisible 'subtle matter', and according to their ideas it was this subtle matter that caused the effects of gravity. On the whole Huygens rested content with this notion. It is surprising to us when we look back upon his work that he did not take more interest in his own results on centrifugal force. For if a satellite moves in a circular path about the earth what constrains it? Huygens, quite as well as Newton, could have answered 'the gravitational attraction between the two bodies'. Perhaps if he had not assumed some kind of fluid pressure to be the cause of gravity he might have anticipated Newton in his great discovery. In Motte's translation of Newton's *Principia* we read (Book I, Proposition 4, Theorem 4) '. . . *Mr. Huygens,* in his excellent book *De Horologio Oscillatorio* [*sic*] has compared the force of gravity with the centrifugal forces of revolving bodies'. Huygens, that is, had actually extended his work into the field that Newton was to treat in so masterly a manner.

On the whole Huygens confined his attention rather more to the mechanics of systems which could be studied in the laboratory. There can be no doubt that Newton alone perceived that there could be a system of mechanics that was universal, that is, one that applied to planets, satellities, tides, the precession of the equinoxes, and also to the collision between bodies in the laboratory, to the properties of compound pendulums and so many other things. It is an amazing experience even today to see how many mathematicians and men of science of that age concentrated their efforts on certain phenomena in order to find, often very laboriously, the answers to particular isolated problems, and then to find Newton dealing with these same problems *en passant* in the *Principia,* deducing the same results in an ordered procession of Propositions and Theorems, so that they are now seen as a part of a much more generalized treatment. Of course it must be remarked that Huygens and others prepared the way for Newton by their specialized studies. Like Bach in music Newton summed up all that had been done before, but his genius went far beyond into a realm that no one before him had entered.

Certainly Huygens's *Horologium Oscillatorium* was never intended as a general treatise on mechanics: its title indicates this clearly enough. The work on centrifugal force referred to by Newton was limited to a statement of certain results which come at the end of the book in a rather disconnected way. The whole of Part II of the book was concerned with the oscillations of a body under gravity. The study of accelerated motion in curved lines was begun by Galileo, and Huygens's work fits on very well as a continuation. Both these writers treated their problems as a branch of 'geometry'. They had come to see them, that is, as quite abstract problems, many of them concerned with conditions which it would be very difficult to realize in the laboratory.

There is much in Galileo's writings about the time it takes a small body to descend along an inclined plane and along an arc of a circle. After a body has fallen through a given vertical height—along any chosen path—it must possess enough kinetic energy (to use our modern term) to enable it to re-ascend to the same height as before. Theoretically then, a body could oscillate backwards and forwards in a given curved path indefinitely. There were two questions that interested Huygens and others at that time and they were these: first, is there some special curve along which descent

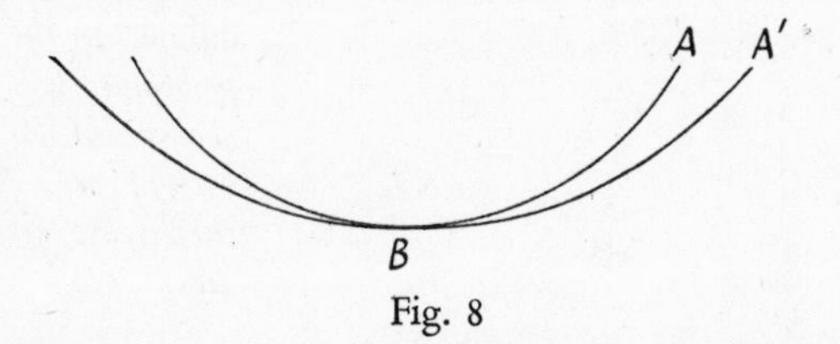

Fig. 8

under gravity from A or A' to B in Fig. 8 is quicker than along any other? and secondly, supposing the curve to be continued so that the body could continue its motion and commence oscillations back and forth, is there a curve in which oscillations *of any amplitude* all take exactly the same time?

Huygens showed that a curve called the cycloid provides the answer to both these questions. If a circle is imagined to roll along the line XY in Fig. 9, a point P on its circumference will trace out

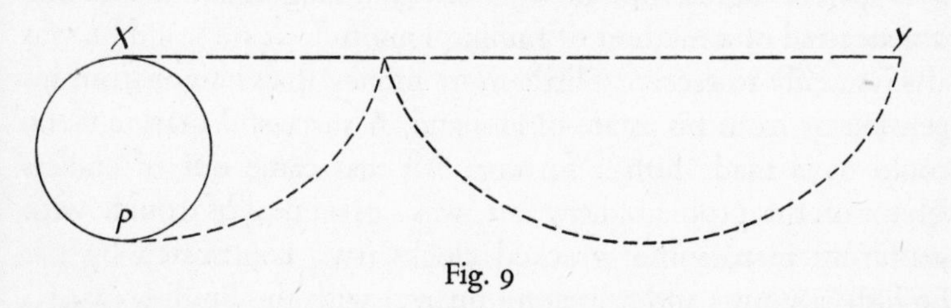

Fig. 9

a curve as shown. This is the cycloid. It was a curve that had attracted the interest of several mathematicians. It gave Huygens much pleasure to work out the geometry associated with this curve and to devise a special type of compound pendulum that would follow a cycloidal path (Fig. 10). This part of his invention proved, in fact, to be of little value. Mathematically neat it was all the same mechanically unsatisfactory. English clockmakers especially developed a new type of escapement which made this refinement superfluous and it is today a mere curiosity.

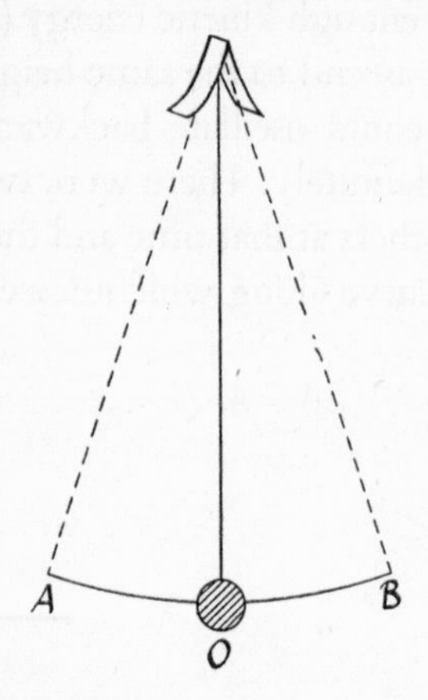

Huygens's cycloidal pendulum. In the figure the pendulum bob swings in a curve AOB which is a cycloid arc. The metal cheeks are also cycloidal arcs.

Fig. 10

In the intervals of a life devotedly spent on exact laboratory experiments in mechanics and optics, and in telescopic observations, we find Huygens going to sea with specially designed pendulum clocks, writing out voluminous directions for sea-captains (in apparent ignorance of their obvious disqualifications as scientists), and with amazing restraint, damning their incompetence. Huygens did not like the sea much, and he hated warfare over patent rights, but he was always being reminded of the urgent need of a method of finding longitude at sea—and he was always ready to receive a little more money than he got from his pension or from his estate in Holland. A successful marine clock could have made him a fortune. All that came out of endless labour on this problem, however, was a great deal of trouble with sea-faring men, some wrecked clocks (two confiscated by the English customs) and a lifelong quarrel with the English experimentalist Robert Hooke, who grumbled about his rival when he met his friends in the coffee shops of London.

Huygens spent the winter of 1670–71 away from Paris through illness and consequently he did not have much to do with the famous Cayenne expedition. This was unfortunate, for about this time things were moving in the scientific world. It is strange to think that some four years earlier than this the young Isaac Newton had already grasped the answer to the chief problem of the solar system—which was how to account for the elliptical orbits of the planets. As yet Newton had not worked the theory out in detail. It is certain that the central idea of a gravitational force due to each mass was not Newton's alone. The French astronomer Boulliau, whom Huygens knew very well, but who was not a member of the inner circle of the Académie Royale des Sciences, as long ago as 1645 had in his *Astronomia Philolaica* proposed that a planetary force, quite contrary to Kepler's theories, must act through the centre of each planet and vary inversely with the square of the distance from the centre. When it was discovered, about this time (1660–70), that a pendulum has slightly different periods of swing at different points on the earth's surface, there were many who considered that this indicated that the earth was not spherical but had a polar diameter which was shorter than the equatorial diameter. Huygens was interested in this problem in 1666, the year of Newton's meditations on the moon's gravity towards the earth, and he was especially interested in the effect of centrifugal force in lessening gravity at the equator.

The second part of this great book *Horologium Oscillatorium* is really a continuation of Galileo's study of natural acceleration. Indeed the first nine propositions are a résumé of his great predecessor's work. Huygens then set out to reach his chief objective: the mathematical proof that the cycloid is the true curve for all oscillations under gravity to be performed in equal times. In the course of this study he first of all introduced in a series of theorems all the necessary pure mathematics: how to construct a tangent at any point on the curve, and so on. When he came to calculate the time taken for a body to descend over a cycloid arc, supposing the necessary constants to be given, Huygens had to overcome the difficulty that such curves could not be measured except by getting the sum of a large number of very small tangents. This is the same kind of problem as computing the distance round a circle. The relationship Huygens established was that the time of descent from any point *A* to the lowest point *B* (Fig. 11) had the same relation to the time of fall from *C* to *B* vertically as one half the circumference of a circle has to the diameter. From this the isochronism of oscillations in a cycloid, that is their taking place in equal times, follows quite simply. But for the reader of the original work there are some twenty-five propositions compared with which Euclid is relatively easy reading.

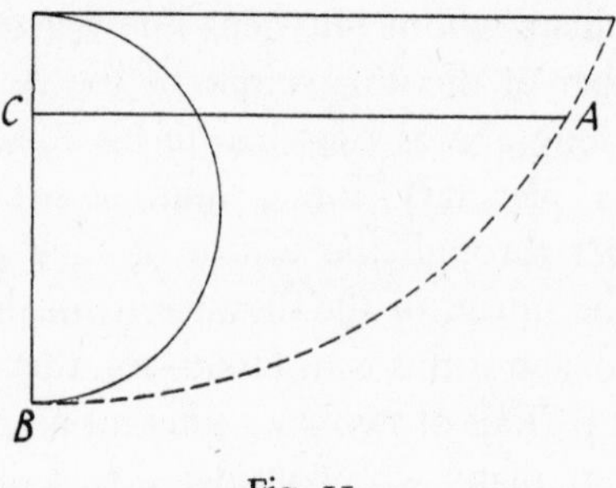

Fig. 11

The reason why Huygens devoted so much time to this problem is interesting. First of all, of course, it was the class of problem which could not be solved very well by a simple experiment. It is difficult to get a body to oscillate in a cycloid, and still more so in those days to show that the time of oscillation was constant, for things like stop watches did not exist. But another reason is quite clearly this: scientists had adopted the rigorous mathematical method as the means by which exact information could be extracted from experiments which were inevitably subject to errors. This was the new mathematical method founded by Galileo and perfected by Huygens and Newton.

The same interest attaches to Part IV of the *Horologium Oscillatorium* (Part III is purely mathematical) which has to do with the problem of the centre of the oscillation. The centre of oscillation can be explained as follows. If we set up an ordinary clock pendulum, consisting of a rigid rod carrying a large mass at its lower end how fast will it swing? What length must the rod be, for example, and where should the mass be placed, if the pendulum is to swing exactly once every second? The time of swing of a *simple* pendulum was known to be connected with its length by the relationship $t \propto \sqrt{l}$. The question is, for any rigid pendulum, such as a rigid uniform bar, to know the length of a *simple* pendulum that will have the same period. There must be a point at which the mass of the rigid (or compound) pendulum might be imagined to be concentrated without altering its period of swing. This point was of obvious theoretical importance in time-keeping and in certain other connexions. It is called the centre of oscillation. This problem was, however, beyond a simple experimental approach unless restricted to a few simple shapes. Even if exact experimental tests had been possible, Huygens and all men of science since his time would have felt it was just as necessary, indeed essential, to establish the law mathematically by reasoning from fundamental principles. Huygens found here, in fact, that he could not deal with the problem in its most general form. He was obliged to fall back on a simple inductive method. He found the centre of oscillation of a number of simple geometrical solids by experiment and then looked for some clue amongst the results. Only long afterwards was he able to give a formal theoretical proof, the difficulty of which was considerable.

Once again Huygens starts where Galileo left off. No experiments are mentioned, but that is because these are the scaffolding on which the building was erected and which was afterwards dismantled. Instead Huygens introduced an important theoretical idea which can be only briefly mentioned here. This means in effect that we cannot get mechanical *work* done for nothing. On this idea of *work* or rather of *energy*, Huygens built a great deal of valuable mechanics. It enabled him to solve this intricate problem and to treat many others in a convincing theoretical manner.

The last part of the great treatise need not detain us, for it was simply a statement of a number of theorems or laws concerning motion in a circle. The mathematical equation for centrifugal force is not proved and Huygens left this problem during his lifetime for others to attempt as best they could. When Newton read the *Horologium Oscillatorium* this equation was really the most important thing for him in the whole book. It appears very probable that he had discovered the same equation independently; it was of course an integral part of his gravitation theory of the moon's motion. When Huygens sent Newton a copy of his book in 1673, however, he could not know how closely he had come to a vast and important subject. He thought of Newton rather as the inventor of a reflecting telescope and as the originator of some elegant experiments on the composition of white light. Fourteen years were to pass before Huygens received a copy of the *Principia* and saw how he and Newton had been concerned with problems that were of the very greatest importance for the future of science.

It is impossible in a brief survey like this to do justice to the full range of experiments carried out during the seventeenth century, and we are concerned in this chapter chiefly to see how experiments were used in conjunction with mathematics. There can be little doubt that this union was the most important discovery of the age. Nevertheless some experiments attracted such interest because they attempted to deal directly with questions of philosophical import. The Aristotelian philosophy and the Cartesian both taught that space is a *plenum,* that it is filled with matter in some form or other. A 'void' was impossible, and belief in a void indicated sympathy for Epicureanism, or at any rate for some form of atomism such as was revived in the seventeenth century by some men of science. The members of the Florentine *Accademia del Cimento* repeated the barometric experiments of Toricelli and utilized the space at the top of the barometer to examine phenomena in a vacuum. But the invention of the vacuum pump considerably improved the prospects for this type of inquiry. Hooke and Boyle in England, and Papin and Huygens in France, were foremost in these experiments. It was not difficult to show that the mercury in an ordinary barometer was kept up by pressure of the air, but the pumps were not sufficiently efficient to obtain really low pressures, that used by Boyle lowering the pressure in the receiver to about one inch of mercury.

It was Huygens's experiments that had the most curious consequences. In place of the wooden piston impregnated with wax in Boyle's pump, Huygens's had a brass piston bound with fine flax. It was described by Papin in his book *Nouvelles Expériences du Vide* of 1674. We do not know how efficient it was, but with it the mercury in an inverted tube of some inches in length could be made to descend and it was probably a better instrument than Boyle's. An inverted tube, closed at the top end, containing water, could also be used, when the water was seen to descend. Yet if the water had been boiled, and so 'purged of air', the column could not be made to descend. This effect was later found with mercury also. We know now that considerable cohesion can occur between a liquid and the glass wall of a tube, and considerable force may be needed to break the column of liquid. Though persuaded that a vacuum can exist, Huygens imagined that the anomalous results pointed to the action of a subtle matter which, he presumed, exerted a pressure even after the pressure due to the atmosphere had been almost entirely removed. This seemed to him to be evidence for the Cartesian vortex theory which he never completely abandoned. He accordingly had the unhappy experience, later in life, of looking on in his old age, as the English philosophers cleared the heavens of Descartes's subtle matter.

It is a pity in a restricted survey of this sort that an account cannot be given of Huygens's masterly experimental work in optics. From Kepler onwards experimental work in this subject was carried out with increasing accuracy and refinement. Descartes published in 1637 the discovery of Willebrord Snell (1621) of the constant we now call the refractive index of a material, but the mechanical explanation of the bending of light rays given by Descartes in his *Dioptrique* was a poor one. A valuable criticism of Descartes's treatment was given by Fermat in 1679. From about 1678 onwards Huygens was able to co-ordinate many of the known facts in an ingenious theory which lent itself to geometrical treatment. The announcement of the discovery of double refraction by Bartholinus in 1670 was felt by Huygens to be a challenge to his theory, and elaborate experiments had to be done to clear up the problem. Huygens brought to this work the same union of measurement and calculation as was shown in his experiments in mechanics.

While we have been chiefly concerned with observations and experiments which could be related fairly simply with important theoretical conceptions, by no means all scientific work exhibits this quality. In the seventeenth century quite a lot was written which was purely descriptive, no one at that time being able to say what significance the observations might later be seen to possess. This was especially true of the considerable literature devoted to observations of animals and plants. Writers like Robert Hooke found as much excitement in the revelations of the microscope as in those of the telescope. Hooke's *Micrographia* of 1665 was a very popular work containing matters of interest in chemistry as well as in biology. His drawings introduced a host of readers to a world of extraordinary magnified detail. Insects and infusoria as well as the cell structures of plants were widely studied both in England and on the Continent. It was long, however, before experiments could be carried out on the very small scale demanded by the study of cells and inevitably biological techniques had to wait upon the techniques of chemistry and physics. The greater part of the literature of the seventeenth century devoted to biological matters turns out therefore to be relatively unimportant. There is as much of it as there is devoted to physical science, but it is the physical science of the age that counted most. It seems impossible to imagine conditions in which physical science could have followed upon biology, however much benefit this might have conferred upon the human race.

CHAPTER FIVE

The Newtonian Synthesis

OCCASIONS for attempting a synthesis, a bringing together of analytical ideas, are rare in the whole history of science. The reason for this no doubt lies in the complexity of the explanatory principles employed, each scientist feeling impelled to take certain things for granted and yet not being able, usually, to say just why he feels confident of some things and not of others.[1] It is conceivable that we might have remained content with purely formal, and mainly geometrical, descriptions of phenomena. The step from geometry to science was never really taken in Greek times and in the time of Copernicus we must doubt if there were more than one or two men who felt that a *mechanical* account of the solar system was necessary. Somehow this question of accounting for things in mechanical terms rose to a place of importance and urgency during the late sixteenth and early seventeenth centuries. Broadly speaking, the question might be put 'If events did not take place because of the purposes behind them then how are they caused?' In answering such a question the experimentalists had to move from the general to the particular. Broad philosophical answers could still be invented, and Descartes's chief mistake was that he imagined that the kind of reasoning that could create the subject of geometry could equally well discover the truth about the laws of nature. It was from Galileo that men learned that a small experiment may bring about the downfall of a whole philosophy. It is no doubt for this very good reason that writers have clung so long to the story of the experiment conducted at the leaning tower of Pisa. To do what Galileo is alleged to have done, that is to show that small and large masses descend to the ground equally fast, would have been a good illustration of his methods.

[1]The excellent little book by Toulmin should be consulted for a perceptive view of scientific methods freed from the old intellectual prejudices of nineteenth-century writers. Stephen Toulmin, *The Philosophy of Science* (1953).

By the middle of the seventeenth century scientific ideas presented an appearance of untidiness and of lack of correlation that is common enough in science, but irritating perhaps to philosophically minded men. A good deal was known about levers, and what we now call 'moments', centres of gravity had received much study, and so had the forces acting on bodies when they are placed on inclined planes. As has been explained it was discovered that two forces acting on a body could be represented by a resultant force which is the diagonal of a parallelogram in which the original forces are represented both in direction and magnitude by the sides. Pulleys had been used for a very long time but only then were theoretical methods found (by Stevin and others) which provided an insight into the mechanics involved. Even today the principle of virtual velocities which is implicit in the usual treatment of pulley systems is not taught in schools, although much of this work, including the seventeenth-century study of fluid pressures, is to be found in the elementary books. We find Galileo and Huygens both using ideas which are very fertile in mechanics and yet never properly defining them so that all the terms used in mechanics are properly related, one with another. To generalize the notion of a force, to clarify the meaning of mass and weight, and to clear up the muddle that existed in the study of impact (that is, of *momentum*), were all things that urgently needed to be done. That this could be achieved in mechanics while at the same time the whole theory could be extended to the planetary system, to orbits, tides and all gravitational phenomena, was of course an undreamed-of synthesis or culmination. And it was only very suddenly that such a culmination was seen to be possible. Many men of great ability were drawn into the argument, and it seems clear that some of them saw certain relationships while others concentrated on others. It may be that a general synthesis was felt to be possible by several of them, but if so none felt able to bring it about or show how it could be done. The experimentalist Robert Hooke, for example, was quite incapable of doing it, and Huygens, who had many of the necessary gifts was in bondage too long to Descartes's philosophy. When we look back on the assembled information that existed after the publication of Huygens's *Horologium Oscillatorium* there is no denying that it was very great. Moreover the astronomers and students of mechanics were discovering common ground in some of their inquiries. Both in Paris and in London there were discussions about the part that gravity plays in the motion of the planets. It was becoming commonplace that a mathematical treatment alone could command respect. Ismael Boulliau (1605–94), a French astronomer who has not had the recognition that appears his due, called his most important publication *Astronomia Philolaica* to indicate his belief that Philolaus, a Pythagorean, had been the true founder of modern astronomy. It was from the Pythagoreans that Europe derived its earliest mathematical impetus, from the Epicureans that there came a primitive atomic doctrine. The right combination of free speculation, imagination, and mathematical treatment was at length becoming clearer. At a time when learned works were still printed in Latin the links with classical antiquity must have seemed very strong.

Most of the men who had contributed to science and mathematics had, up to the late sixteenth century, been associated with the courts of monarchs and princes, or at least possessed the independence of the landed gentry in England. It is important, therefore, that the changes of the age, especially in England, somewhat broadened the base of the social pyramid. The Grammar Schools were providing many new entrants for the learned professions. They were historically the most important institutions ever invented in the history of this country since for the first time they offered opportunities for intellectual development to the sons of farmers, merchants and other people in no specially privileged position in society. Considering the circumstances of his youth it was only by the greatest good fortune that Isaac Newton was enabled to pursue his education. It seems likely that he was saved for science and mathematics through the alertness and good sense of Henry Stokes, the headmaster of the King's School, Grantham, where Newton studied as a boy and where he prepared himself to enter Cambridge.

Isaac Newton was born in 1642. It is always remarked that this was the year in which Galileo died. Newton's mother would, however, know nothing of Galileo. The year in which her first child was born was the year in which her husband Isaac had died three months previously at the age of thirty-seven, and it was the year in which England saw the outbreak of civil war. Living in a small manor house at Woolsthorpe, in a remote part of Lincolnshire, Newton grew up in troubled times. The Eastern shires were Parliamentarian and most of the fighting took place in the Midlands and in the West. Nevertheless, it may be as L. T. More suggests in his biography of Newton, that as a boy he 'must have been familiar with the incursions of rough raiding parties after provisions and plunder, and he and his grandmother, suspected of sympathy to the royal forces, must have been frequently forced to avoid embarrassing questions of the Commonwealth soldiers and of the local magistrates'. In January 1649, when Newton was only six, Charles I was executed. In the succeeding years, up to 1661 when Newton went to Cambridge, England experienced a severe dictatorship during which royalist sympathizers had to keep quiet about their opinions. The restoration of the monarchy took place in May 1660.

It was accordingly an eventful time in which Newton grew up. When his mother married a second time after two years, she left her little son to live with his grandmother at Woolsthorpe. Then, when her second husband died in 1656, she returned with three young children of her second marriage to the manor house. Isaac Newton, as the eldest child, might have been expected to help her in her management of the farm, but he showed no aptitude. Hannah was a woman of character and intellect and she appears to have made no difficulties in response to the advice given her by Stokes that Newton should proceed to Cambridge. It was necessary for Isaac to lodge in Grantham during term time and all the indications are that he obtained the necessary grounding in Latin, Greek, ancient history, and a certain amount of mathematics, in spite of the difficulties that stood in the way.

Trinity College, when Newton went there in 1661, was declining somewhat from its former glory. Formerly a great seat of learning and a well-administered college, it sank to surprising depths by the end of the seventeenth century. It is strange that this decline continued during Newton's Fellowship. Charles II and James II filled Fellowships without regard for scholarship or merit and it is not surprising in these circumstances that many of the studies remained scholastic long after the real interests of the age had changed. During Newton's years at Cambridge (1661–96) the universities had to resist the schemes of James II who, at the instigation of a Jesuit sect, tried to get Catholics into positions of power in the colleges. The King would have been glad to have seen the colleges transformed into Catholic seminaries, but fortunately his first move at Cambridge, an attempt to get a Benedictine monk named Alban Francis admitted to the degree of Master of Arts excited intense resistance. Newton was one of the Fellows who represented the university on this occasion. Later he was elected Member of Parliament for the university. As L. T. More points out, Newton was not by choice a secluded student of science and mathematics. When the opportunity came he readily sought friendship with eminent men and was quite ready to fill an important public position. When finally he left Cambridge where all his greatest work was written he did so without an expression of regret.

Newton's connexion with the university came to an end when he was made Master of the Mint. He was happy to move to London. In 1703 he was elected President of the Royal Society and thereafter he was re-elected to this office annually up to his death. The story of Newton's life therefore is one that leads from an obscure origin to a considerable public position. This position he won through intellectual distinction, for he had in his lifetime European fame. His best biography is an account of his intellectual life. Although much has been written about him, his character and personality remain shrouded in a good deal of uncertainty. L. T. More believes that Newton's relations with his colleagues at Cambridge were never more than formal, but More emphasizes Newton's success in attracting and encouraging young and able students during the years he was Lucasian Professor of Mathematics. Amongst these were Roger Cotes who edited the second edition of the *Principia,* Edmund Halley, John Keill, and Charles Montague, afterwards Earl of Halifax. Next to Montague, says More, Newton's most congenial friends were Henry More and John Locke. Unfortunately Newton's manner was cold and unfriendly, sometimes towards men who helped him most. This was particularly true of his relationship with the Astronomer

Royal, John Flamsteed. While, therefore, he was widely admired in later life he seems never to have been held in warm affection except by the younger men he encouraged. He conceded little to his great predecessors in the fields of mathematics and science and he made few allowances for the difficulties of others who no doubt lacked his superlative intellectual gifts. 'I want not your calculations, but your observations only,' he wrote impatiently to the Astronomer Royal. '. . . I will therefore once more propose it to you, to send me your naked observations of the moon's right ascensions and meridional altitudes; and leave it to me to get the places calculated from them.' Newton remains a complex character and the reader who wishes to study him should turn to the biography by L. T. More or the writings of Professor E. N. da C. Andrade. He never married and after he entered Cambridge he seems to have devoted all his energies as a young man to intense intellectual effort. His achievement was superb and remains to this day unsurpassed. Whether these efforts exacted a toll from him, affecting his nervous stability and his personal relationships, we may never know.

Newton was at Cambridge about a year and a half before Isaac Barrow took up the new Professorship of Mathematics. When Barrow arrived, however, he became Newton's tutor and in this capacity was responsible for his pupil's course of study. It was extremely fortunate that Newton at this early age was guided by one of the few men at the university who knew what was happening in the world of scientific and mathematical ideas. Besides Galileo and Kepler, Descartes and Fermat, Newton would accordingly hear of others including Huygens, whose work, as yet unpublished, had aroused the interest of the French and English scientific societies. Yet Barrow had only a short time in which to assist his remarkable pupil for, at the end of the summer term 1665, Trinity College had to dismiss its students owing to the dangers of the plague. Since the visitation of 1630 it was realized that dispersal of the students was the only measure which could be taken with the dread infection. And so in 1665 and 1666, while the plague raged in London, and the colleges at Cambridge were closed, Newton remained in the country at his home at Woolsthorpe, south of Grantham. Here he worked out some of the details of two major discoveries; the theory of fluxions in mathematics, and the theory of universal gravity. When he left Cambridge in June 1665 he left behind him a third most valuable achievement: a reflecting telescope partly completed.

Unfortunately it is difficult to do justice to the theory of fluxions in non-mathematical language. The first step was taken by Descartes when he showed that a curved line could be represented by an algebraic equation between two quantities whose changes are connected with each other in a regular manner. Thus $y = x^2$ represents a curve which is a parabola:

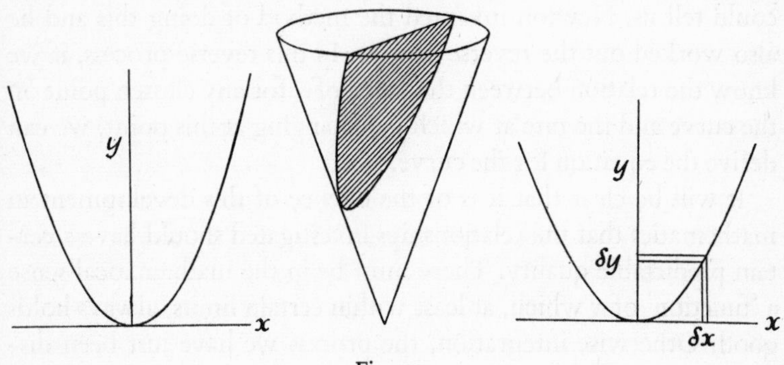

Fig. 12

This curve is an example of certain curves which interested Greek mathematicians because they are conic sections. The second figure shows the same figure as the outline of a suitably chosen section of a cone. At the beginning of the seventeenth century Galileo has shown that a projectile follows a path which is a parabola. Kepler introduced the ellipse into theoretical astronomy. In England and France new studies in dynamics dealt with motion in curves and consequently with changing velocities. Newton was later to be asked by his friend Edmund Halley to work out by mathematics the path of a planet travelling round the sun under an inverse square law of attractive force. He was able to show that this would be an ellipse in the general case, but such problems required a branch of mathematics capable of dealing, not with fixed relationships between two variables but with changing relationships. The rate of change of y with x in Fig. 12, shown at a given portion of the curve, may be represented by the fraction $\frac{\delta y}{\delta x}$ where δy and δx represent very small intervals on the two axes of the graph. As the length of the tangent is narrowed down, until ideally it touches the curve at only the point of contact the quantities δy and δx become vanishingly small. We then represent them by the symbols dy and dx and the rate of change is shown as $\frac{dy}{dx}$. If we have an equation, such as $y = x^2$ it should be possible to decide how fast y is changing with respect to x at any required point, and this far more accurately than any geometrical method could tell us. Newton invented the method of doing this and he also worked out the reverse process. In this reverse process, if we know the relation between the value of x for any chosen point on the curve and the rate at which y is changing at this point, we can derive the equation for the curve.

It will be clear that it is of the essence of this development in mathematics that the relationships investigated should have a certain predictable quality. There must be in the mathematical sense a 'function' of x which, at least within certain limits, always holds good. Otherwise integration, the process we have just been discussing, could not be carried out. Fortunately the curves (or equations) which the mathematicians met in their studies in dynamics did prove relatively simple although, as we have seen, they were not all conics. Early in Book I of his *Principia* Newton indicated the principle of integration in finding the areas of certain figures. He called this section 'The method of first and last ratios of quantities, by the help whereof we demonstrate the propositions that follow'. In his figure he divides the area into a number of oblong strips (Fig. 13), working first on the outside of the curve and then on the inside. This gives the two outlines in which the curve has been replaced by a series of steps. When the number of oblongs is made greater and greater, and they become narrower and narrower, ultimately, says Newton, their areas must become the same. It is simply a question, then, of finding a formula for the area of the oblongs as they are made narrower and narrower. At this point Newton tells us no more about his method. He does not give his notation although it seems certain that he must have used the differential and integral calculus in his investigations. In the *Principia* he presents his Propositions and Theorems so far as possible in geometrical form.

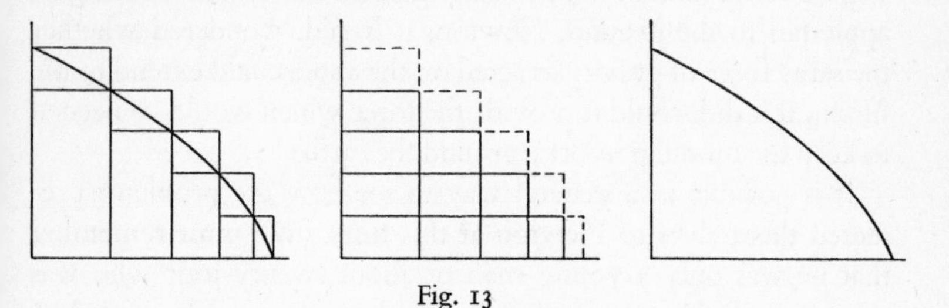

Fig. 13

It is impossible to overestimate the importance of the differential and integral calculus at this period in the history of science. The problems arising at the time were of the sort that demanded quite new mathematical resources, and it is clear that these problems stimulated the mathematicians in their efforts to find new methods. Newton and Leibnitz independently, and it appears in rather different ways, discovered the principles of integration and differentiation. Yet, nevertheless, it is worth remarking that it was fortunate, to say the least, that the relationships which are of the greatest importance in the dynamics of the seventeenth century were not more complex than they were. It has often been fortunate in scientific work that the effects first observed have appeared simpler than they really are. A notable exception, perhaps, must be made, of the facts about the moon's motion. These from the first were found by Newton to be complicated and the details of the moon's motion occupied him long after the *Principia* was published. It was, it seems, the one subject which made his head ache and caused him sleeplessness. Planetary theory was fortunately less difficult. In the earliest speculations about gravitational attraction it was assumed that a planet goes round the sun in an ellipse without causing any movement in the sun itself. Gravity is simply the 'string' which retains the planet and prevents it from flying off at a tangent. Fortunately the sun is so massive that this simplification is not at first a serious misrepresentation. Newton's treatment allows for the mutual gravitational effects of both bodies. It is not the sun which remains stationary but the common centre of gravity of the whole solar system. But much remained to be done before his initial idea, which may go back to the fall of an apple in the orchard at Woolsthorpe, could be developed to the stage we find in the *Principia*. Sitting in the orchard, and seeing an apple fall to the ground, Newton, it is said, wondered whether the same force of gravity as acted on the apple could extend to the moon. If it did, could it provide the force which would be needed to keep the moon in its orbit around the earth?

It is possible in a general way to see how the problems presented themselves to Newton at this time. (We must remember that he was only a young man of about twenty-four who was then quite unknown in the world of science and learning.) A force which in some way issues from a centre and affects any material body at a distance d from it must decrease as d increases. Moreover it is practically certain that the force will diminish, not in proportion to d but to d^2. An inverse square law, then, would appear extremely probable. Thus the force would be very much reduced at the distance of the moon. But then the moon is a large mass—far greater than any terrestrial body. How would that affect the result? Newton must have decided straight away that the force of gravity between two bodies must be proportional to the masses of *both* bodies. One might express this by the equation

$$F = G.\frac{m_1 m_2}{d^2}$$

where m_1 and m_2 are the masses attracting each other and d is their distance apart. If we left out the constant G we should have to replace the $=$ sign by one for proportionality. G is called the 'gravitational constant'.

All this looks fairly simple, as it is represented in the pages of modern text-books. But we must remember the great difficulties in the way at that time. In 1665 there was no definition of *force* which was of any use for problems in dynamics; and m_1 and m_2 represent only small masses whose diameters are small compared with their distance apart. The moon is of course a long way from the earth. But in the only circumstances under which measurements of acceleration under gravity could be made, that is on the surface of the earth, we have a very different state of affairs. Can we possibly suppose the mass of the earth, for such problems, can be supposed to be located at its centre? This is the famous 'gravitating sphere' problem. Newton was later able to prove that the gravitational effect of a large spherical body can be calculated on the assumption that all the mass is concentrated at the centre. It seems likely that Newton supposed that the result could (in 1665 or 1666) be taken for granted. He left the problem of proving this theorem for about twenty years.

What, then, would Newton have at this point in his reflections? The acceleration of a body falling under gravity near the earth's surface is known to be 32 ft. per sec. per sec. The usual symbol for the acceleration of gravity is g. If we take the radius of the earth to be r and the radius of the moon's orbit (assumed circular) to be R, then, applying our inverse square law we get:

$$\frac{g}{g'}=\frac{R^2}{r^2}$$

where g' represents the acceleration due to the earth's gravity at the distance of the moon. Since values for g, R and r were all available in 1666 Newton could calculate the value of g'. It would then remain to see if the result agreed with the centrifugal force acting on unit mass of the moon. For this he must have got Huygens's formula independently; and then, using the values then accepted for R, it appears he made the calculation and found the results to 'answer pretty nearly'. The reason for the twenty years' delay in settling this fascinating question is, according to the opinion most often accepted today, simply that the 'gravitating sphere' problem remained to be solved.

On returning to Cambridge in 1667 Newton was elected to a minor fellowship at Trinity; in March 1668 he became a senior Fellow of the College, and in 1669 he succeeded Barrow as Lucasian Professor. Although he was now a professor of mathematics, he considered the subject as an end in itself to be dry and barren. He valued it, says L. T. More, 'only as a tool and a language for the expression of natural law'. It is curious that he did not much admire the new Cartesian geometry. As a consequence he did not press the claims of the method of fluxions which he had himself developed out of it. Instead, therefore, of lecturing on the solar system and gravity, even instead of publishing anything on these subjects, Newton chose to develop his work in optics. It was this work and the construction of the reflecting telescope which Newton chose first to send to the Royal Society, and it was for this that he first became known in Paris as well as in London. The reflecting telescope was indeed the outcome of his studies of white light and colours, for he became convinced that lenses could not be freed from the effect of dispersion. Galileo's telescopes, and Huygens's, produced images which were fringed with colours and this of course seriously affected the clearness of the image. Instead of using lenses to bring the rays to a focus, Newton, following a suggestion made first by James Gregory, and in a slightly different form by Cassegrain in France, used a concave spherical mirror. The only difficulty in this case is that the image is formed at the principal focus of the mirror and the rays have to be reflected out through the side of the telescope so as to enter the eye of the observer. Neither Gregory nor Cassegrain brought their idea to any practical success, but Newton's telescope, made with his own hands, succeeded remarkably well for its small size, and it was only the difficulty attending the grinding of mirrors and of silvering the top surface which discouraged men like Huygens from adopting it.

For most purposes Newton supposed light to be a stream of corpuscles travelling at a very great speed in straight lines. In England Robert Hooke, and in France Huygens, had worked out their own 'wave theories', assuming the existence of a subtle matter to transmit the vibrations. Huygens's and Hooke's theories were quite independent, but as a point of history they both owed something to Descartes's ideas. Newton did not accept the pulse or wave theory of Huygens, it appears, partly because certain effects, which would be expected from a wave property of light, had not then been detected and also, perhaps, because he was sceptical about all Descartes's notions. Nevertheless he was himself driven to wonder if there is not some sort of 'ether'. Writing to Oldenburg at the end of 1675 he certainly expressed himself very definitely against the ether. 'I must first . . . cast out what he [Hooke] has borrowed from Descartes and others, viz. that there is an ethereal medium; that is less implicated in the parts of solid bodies, and so moves freely in them and transmits light more readily through them. . . . This, I think, is, in short, the sum of his hypothesis, and in all this I have nothing in common with him. . . .' Nevertheless, after he had discovered that heat can travel through a vacuum, Newton did question whether there is not some ethereal medium. The 'Queries' which he appended to his *Optics,* published in 1706, are the best sources of his ideas, and they show that both in regard to light and also in regard to gravity, Newton was not consistently opposed to views such as Huygens held.

On 18 February 1675 Newton paid his first visit to the Royal Society. It is difficult to say that he had many close friends in the society, and easier to say that he made enemies. Hooke in particular found himself ousted by Newton's scientific work much as he found himself ousted by Huygens in the matter of the spring-regulated clock and the problems concerning cycloidal and conical pendulums which he tried in vain to solve for himself. The truth in this matter was that Hooke was an ingenious experimenter but no mathematician and his chagrin might almost be taken to illustrate the lot of the man who tackles science without mathematics ever since the beginning of the seventeenth century. Hooke wrote to Newton in 1679 to suggest that systematic observations of the heavens should be made at Cambridge as well as at London, instancing the new ventures of the Paris Academy, and he acquainted Newton with the latest speculations about the solar system which had gained attention on the Continent. In his reply Newton made a suggestion which had an important sequel. We have to remember that thirteen years had gone by since Newton had made his preliminary calculations on the theory of the moon's gravity towards the earth and he had made nothing public. The Cartesian vortices were still accepted by Hooke, Huygens and others. One hundred and thirty-seven years had passed since Copernicus died and yet no incontrovertible proof had been discovered for the earth's motion and a diurnal rotation. Newton then wrote to suggest a delicate experiment in which, according to theory, a small object dropped from a great height should fall a little to the east of the perpendicular (Fig. 14). This is because the linear velocity v' is greater than v and consequently when the body

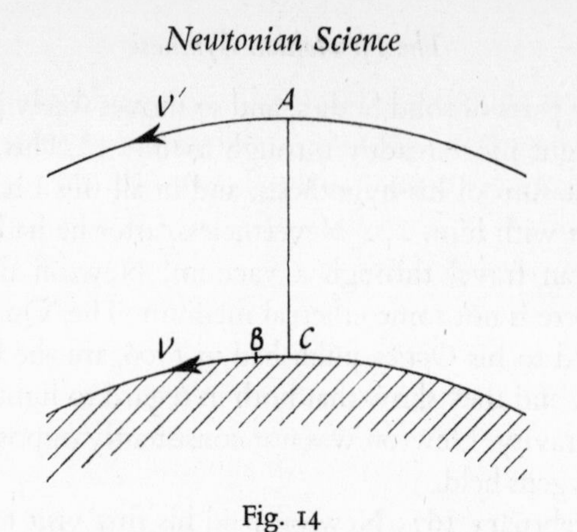

Fig. 14

falls it reaches a point *B* to the east of *C* which is perpendicularly below *A*. Newton stated that the body would fall along a line which forms part of a spiral curve towards the centre of the earth.

At a meeting of the Royal Society Hooke explained Newton's suggestion to an extremely interested audience. Then, at the next meeting, he criticized Newton's theory because it omitted to take into account the northerly latitude of London. This, he argued, would cause the body to fall a little to the south as well as to the east. It seems to be an innocent correction and not a very great matter. Yet it provoked a long hostility between Newton and Hooke. This had the effect, however, of stirring Newton out of his old indifference to problems he had set aside. He saw, no doubt, that several men were in possession of promising ideas on gravity and its application to the planetary orbits, but that what was lacking was the mathematical treatment.

Fortunately other events occurred at this stage which impelled Newton in the same direction and led in due course to his writing the *Principia*. In 1680 a striking comet appeared in the sky. Night after night it was carefully observed by astronomers of whom Flamsteed, the Astronomer Royal, was chief. Flamsteed noticed that the comet approached the sun as it moved across the night sky and there followed a period in which it became invisible. A few weeks later, however, the comet returned to visibility but moving in a different direction. Flamsteed felt confident that the second comet was the same as the first. Newton, surprisingly and obstinately, would not for a long time agree with Flamsteed although the latter was able to produce very strong evidence for his conclusion. At length Newton was convinced. It was not clear, however, how comets fitted into the Copernican theory and in fact the whole theory of the solar system was at that time in a thoroughly unsatisfactory state.

Nevertheless, as late as 1681 there was little or nothing to indicate that Newton was meditating a comprehensive treatise on dynamics and the solar system. The *Philosophical Transactions* and the *Journal des Savants* contained many communications bearing on the new subject of dynamics begun by Galileo and Huygens and there were several men of science in England who by this time were alive to the possibility that dynamical equations might be applied to the motions of the planets. Hooke, Wren and Halley, to mention only three of the chief, were dissatisfied with Kepler's laws which were geometrical in form. They looked for explanations involving appropriate forces. Halley in particular believed that the gravitation of planets towards the sun was the cause of the elliptical orbits and he saw that if there was an inverse square law of force it ought to be possible to prove that an elliptical path would be followed by a planet. Sir Christopher Wren offered a prize of forty shillings to Hooke and Halley if they could prove the theorem, but it was too difficult. Halley six months later took the problem to Newton at Cambridge. According to John Conduitt, who collected material for a biography of Newton and who lived at Newton's house during the last ten years of the scientist's life, Halley 'at once indicated the object of his visit by asking Newton what would be the curve described by the planets on the supposition that gravity diminished as the square of the distance. Newton immediately answered, *an ellipse*. Struck with joy and amazement, Halley asked him how he knew it. Why, replied he, I have calculated it; and being asked for the calculation, he could not find it, but promised to send it to him.' This, after a short delay, Newton did. Newton later gave some lectures at Cambridge on the subject of the planetary orbits and it was this work which provided the germ of the *Principia*.

The *Principia* is universally acknowledged to be the greatest single achievement in the history of science. The writing of it took about seventeen months during which Newton is said to have been scarcely aware of the ordinary matters of life. Much credit must be given to his friend Edmund Halley who throughout this period was always ready to give encouragement. Halley undertook to pay for the publication of the work and this must have placed a great strain on his slender resources. He throughout acted tactfully in preventing Newton from experiencing the effects of Hooke's jealousy whenever he could. Difficulties had to be avoided with Flamsteed also, for Flamsteed supplied Newton with valuable astronomical data. Unfortunately Newton did not reward Flamsteed by recognizing his contribution to the theory of comets as he might have done. It has been said that Newton deliberately made the *Principia* difficult to read so as to exclude non-mathematicians (a large body) from his critics. There may have been other important reasons. To a large extent the style of dynamical studies is determined by the nature of the subject and both Galileo and Huygens had shown how such works could be written. Huygens's *Horologium Oscillatorium* especially impressed Newton and in this work one has, in effect, the true prototype of large scientific publications such as Newton and Laplace were to write. It is therefore surprising that Newton did not acknowledge the work of Galileo and Huygens, his forerunners, in generous terms.

We approach now the task of saying briefly what the *Principia* contains and trying to make good its inevitable neglect by modern readers, who should nevertheless understand its great historical as well as scientific significance. Fortunately Professor Florian Cajori has issued a modern form of the second edition (in the eighteenth-century English translation). This contains the interesting preface by Newton's pupil Roger Cotes. This edition was an improvement on the first because Cotes saw in what ways Newton's outlook needed to be explained. The Cartesians, Cotes explained, 'take a liberty of imagining at pleasure unknown figures and magnitudes, and uncertain situations and motions of the parts, and moreover of supposing occult fluids, freely pervading the pores of bodies . . .', they 'assume hypotheses as first principles'. Leibnitz's philosophy had become known in England since the date of the first edition, and Cotes crossed swords with him also. He was scornful that anyone could believe that 'the force alone of his mind, and the internal light of his reason' could establish the laws of the universe or could imagine that he himself 'a miserable reptile, can tell what is fittest to be done'. Leibnitz had argued in effect that since God had established the best possible world we should be able to discover what its laws must be. This appeared to the Newtonians a great piece of presumption.

The Preface to the *Principia* opens with some preliminary definitions (of mass, quantity of motion or momentum, force and means of measuring force) and other matters which clear the way for mathematical relationships of a verifiable kind but do not avoid certain philosophical difficulties. Newton emphasizes that in dealing with forces his interest is mathematical rather than physical. He saw his goal clearly enough, also, in defining mathematical time which 'flows equably without relation to anything external', and relative time which is 'some sensible and external (whether accurate or unequable) measure of duration by the means of motion, which is commonly used instead of true time. . . .' Absolute space and relative space are then considered in a similar way, for he wished to clear away difficulties about absolute and relative motion and rest. Nevertheless he did not dispose of these problems very satisfactorily. One is left with a belief that his absolute quantities cannot be justified by what he says of them.

Then come his well-known laws of motion, a statement of what is known as the parallelogram rule, and a statement of the law of conservation of momentum. There is no doubt of Newton's indebtedness to Huygens in several matters, for the latter disseminated views which reached the Royal Society and were generally adopted. Much has been written about Newton's three laws of motion. They state (*a*) that left to itself, without any disturbing force, a body continues at rest or else moves indefinitely at constant velocity, that is, with constant speed in a straight line; (*b*) that if a force acts on a body its 'momentum' is changed at a rate which depends on the size of the force acting, and in the direction in which it acts; (*c*) that 'action' and 'reaction' are equal.

To explain these laws satisfactorily is rather a technical matter, and it is somewhat difficult to arouse excitement at the perusal of them in modern times. Nor can the subject be enlivened by satisfactory experiments except in certain limited respects. We all know that a gun recoils on firing, which illustrates the third law qualitatively, but the conservation of momentum is not easily demonstrated. What we have to remember is that this unification of ideas in mechanics, represented by Newton's *Principia,* cleared away the muddles and confusions of centuries. The idea that a force is needed to keep a body in motion is gone for ever, so is the notion that anything is needed to keep a body rotating. On the contrary, both for motion in a straight line, or rotation on an axis, force must be used to slow a body down. The laws not only define force but provide a measure of it. That is, the laws lay down the quantitative relationships and bring mathematics to bear on the whole subject. When we think how, from the time of Aristotle down to the publication of the *Principia,* men had speculated about 'natural' and 'unnatural' motions, and had been ready to accept circular motions as part of the eternal natural scheme of things so that they required no other explanation, then we shall perhaps begin to see the force of Newton's treatment. According to Newton matter is anything that possesses inertia. A force is needed to accelerate a piece of matter, and it accelerates it in the direction of the straight line in which the force acts. The mass of a body can be measured by its inertia, or alternatively by its weight. These two alternatives came into the Newtonian scheme from the beginning.

The chief subject of Book I is the mechanics of the planetary orbits. If a body moves in any curve which is a conic, that is, a circle, ellipse, parabola or hyperbola, about a stationary body situated at the focus, an inverse square law of attractive force will account for the motion. This assumes the bodies to be massive particles of negligible volume. Newton's method is to proceed from one Proposition, with its attendant Theorems, to another. The work is built up after the manner of Euclid's geometry, each part that comes later depending on what has gone before. Every now and again, however, Newton gives what he calls a *Scholium.* In a *Scholium,* he does not establish any proof but explains in general terms what the argument is about and how he intends to proceed. One can get some idea of the *Principia* by reading the *Scholia* for it is a severe test of one's concentration and ability in geometry to read through the Propositions and Theorems. Half-way through Book I we find him ending Section 3 with the words: 'So far concerning the finding of the orbits. It remains that we determine the motions of the bodies in the orbits so found.' Thus the orbits are thought of as quite abstract geometrical figures. This point of view had long been traditional in astronomy. At the end of Section 8 we read: 'I have hitherto considered the motions of bodies in immoveable orbits. It remains now to add something concerning their motions in orbits which revolve round the centres of force.'

'I have hitherto been treating of the attractions of bodies towards an immoveable centre; tho' very probably there is no such thing existent in nature,' Newton remarks in Section 11. 'For attractions are made towards bodies; and the actions of the bodies attracted and attracting, are always reciprocal and equal by law 3. So that if there are two bodies, neither the attracted nor the attracting body is truly at rest, but both (by Cor. 4 of the laws of motion) being as it were mutually attracted, revolve about a common centre of gravity. . . .' The dynamical aspects of planetary theory were in this part of the work interesting him more particularly and we move on in a few more pages to the famous Proposition concerning the gravitating sphere (Proposition 70, Theorem 30). This proved that no force acts on a particle within a hollow sphere, and it follows that a particle is attracted towards a solid sphere as if the mass of the latter were concentrated at its centre. These are some of the most striking things in Book I. In it many problems, such as Saturn's ring, the tides, the shape of the earth, and the precession of the equinoxes, are dealt with mathematically for the first time. Precession, for example, results from a slight rotation of the axis of the earth so that this does not point constantly towards the pole star but describes a slow conical rotation, the south pole rotating in the opposite sense. This is a consequence of the flattening of the earth towards the poles.

In the whole of Book I the resistance of any medium to motion occurring in it is ignored. The planets certainly appear not to be resisted. Practically the whole of Book II, however, is taken up with the motion of bodies in a resisting medium. For while

Newton had shown in Book I how gravity would account for planetary motion he had not disproved the Cartesian theory which might, therefore, continue as an alternative. Cote's preface to the second edition, however, refers to the absurdity of suggesting relationships which are not expressed quantitatively in a theory of the solar system, and Newton, as he applied himself to the Cartesian vortices, clearly intended to explode this plausible theory. Thus he considered the effect of viscosity on the velocity of a body entering a medium with a given momentum, and resisted in proportion to its velocity (Proposition 2, Theorem 2). Then he took a body falling under gravity through such a medium and this enabled him to discuss the path of a projectile in a resisting medium. Newton considered, however, that the case of a resistance varying with the square of the velocity was more important and he repeated his calculations on this new basis. Then he took 'The Circular Motions of Bodies in Resisting Mediums'.

At this point Newton appears to go away from his main argument and describe experiments with pendulums moving in a resisting medium. This was, however, evidence of an experimental nature against the existence of a subtle matter. There followed an account of the kinetic theory of fluids and some theorems concerning spherical masses moving in fluids. Much of this work has obvious value in the laboratory and has found repeated application. An interesting example was Newton's study of the solid of least resistance to the flow of a medium past it. Much as the modern engineer constructs a wind tunnel he supposes the body to be at rest and determines the force acting on it owing to the medium sent against it. The curve which must be rotated about an axis to generate the solid of least resistance has an obvious relation with the design of shells and rocket projectiles. *En passant* Newton revealed the difficulties of Descartes's theory of light as a pressure transmitted through the particles of a fluid.

At last Newton turns to fluids and vortex motion. The movement of a fluid in a vortex will not account for Kepler's laws (Proposition 52). 'If a solid sphere, in a uniform and infinite fluid, revolves about an axis given in position with a uniform motion, and the fluid be forced round by only this impulse of the sphere;

and every part of the fluid perseveres uniformly in its motion: I say, that the periodic times of the parts of the fluid are as the squares of their distances from the centre of the sphere.' Furthermore, the vortex motion set up must 'by degrees be propagated onwards *in infinitum*'. Unless, therefore, there is some source of motion, the rotating sphere would come gradually to rest. There follow other detailed objections to Descartes's (and Huygens's) theory. The neighbouring globes, each rotating, would tend to move each other. Applied to the case of Jupiter's satellites the periodic times do not agree with theory in the least. 'Hence it is manifest that the planets are not carried round in corporeal vortices; for according to the *Copernican* hypothesis, the planets going round the sun revolve in ellipses, having the sun in their common focus; and by radii drawn to the sun describe areas proportional to the times. But the parts of a vortex can never revolve with such a motion.' This was an excellent example of the use of mathematical methods in examining an hypothesis.

In Book III, entitled *Of the System of the World,* Newton explains that he will now 'demonstrate the frame of the System of the World'. So much uncertainty seemed to surround the procedure which he advocated, however, especially as a result of Cartesian philosophizing, that Newton first gives what he considers to be 'The Rules of Reasoning in Philosophy'. Perhaps the most interesting remark he makes is this: 'In experimental philosophy we are to look upon propositions inferred by general induction from phenomena as accurately or very nearly true, notwithstanding any contrary hypothesis which may be imagined, till such time as other phenomena occur, by which they may either be made more accurate, or liable to exceptions.' 'This rule we must follow, that the argument of induction may not be evaded by hypothesis.' He inserts into his Rules, however, a powerful plea for the recognition of the principle of mutual gravitation between bodies. 'Lastly, if it universally appears, by experiments and astronomical observations, that all bodies about the Earth, gravitate towards the Earth; and that in proportion to the quantity of matter which they severally contain; that the Moon likewise, according to the quantity of its matter, gravitates towards the Earth; that on the other hand our Sea gravitates towards the

Moon; and all the Planets mutually one towards another; and the Comets in like manner towards the Sun; we must, in consequence of this rule, universally allow, that all bodies whatsoever are endowed with a principle of mutual gravitation.'

This book, as a whole, is a development of the ideas of the first. The idea of universal gravitation, that every particle attracts every other particle with a force diminishing with the square of the distance, is given wide application. The moon's gravity balances its centrifugal force, and this is true of all other bodies moving in central orbits. Comets are shown to fall into line, and it is shown that if there is any fluid resistance to planetary motions it must be exceedingly slight. Detailed studies of the diameters of the planetary orbits then follow: orbital eccentricities, the moon's libration, the flattening of the earth at the poles, and the variation of the gravitational force over the surface of the earth, the disturbance of the moon's orbit owing to the sun, these and other technical matters are dealt with in quite a readable style despite their difficulty, and in a setting which is magnificent. In this book there is more marshalling of evidence in a general discourse and less of theoretical geometrical proof. This makes Book III in many ways the most attractive part of the *Principia*. Newton explained in his Introductory remarks that he had intended it to be a popular work but that on reflection he had reduced its substance. He recommended that the third book could be read on its own provided that the reader studied the definitions, the laws of motion, and the first three sections of Book I.

At the end of Book III, in the second edition but not in the first, there comes a summing up of the purpose and achievement of the work. Descartes's system has been shown to be untenable: 'The hypothesis of Vortices is press'd with many difficulties,' he says, and he goes on to show how exceedingly formidable they are. They are in fact fatal to the theory. Instead, a universal force of gravity accounts for the chief phenomena. This is not, however, to return to some kind of Epicurean scheme, some sort of mechanism operating under the play of blind and indifferent forces. Newton is quite definite about this. 'This most beautiful system of the sun, planets and comets, could only proceed from the counsel and dominion of an intelligent and powerful Being.' Gravity, however, he cannot explain. And he adds, reverting to his rules for reasoning: 'I frame no hypotheses; for whatever is not deduced from the phenomena is to be called an hypothesis; and hypotheses whether metaphysical or physical, whether of occult properties or mechanical, have no place in experimental philosophy.' 'In this philosophy', Newton goes on, 'particular propositions are inferr'd from the phenomena, and afterwards rendered general by induction. Thus it was that the impenetrability, the mobility, and the impulsive force of bodies, and the laws of motion and of gravitation, were discovered. And to us it is enough, that gravity does really exist, and act according to the laws which we have explained, and abundantly serves to account for all the motions of the celestial bodies, and of our sea.'

Yes, the *Principia* is a scientific and philosophical work on the grandest scale. Having put forth this great effort in clarifying and systematizing the subject matter of mechanics it is understandable that Newton should feel strongly about the true methods of science. It is of the greatest interest, therefore, that he failed to convince some of the best minds of his time. Huygens, for example, thought that universal gravity was an occult quality, and one may suppose that he heard Newton's claim that he did not invent hypotheses with something like amusement. Was not this universal gravity itself a most bizarre hypothesis? Could one conceive such a thing? Could not the huge rotating vortices be conceived far more easily? And did not that argue for their truth? So strong was this habit of mind that many besides Huygens hesitated over the Newtonian system and in fact refused for very many years to accept it. Leibnitz outdid Huygens in his opposition to Newton's theory of universal gravitation. He believed quite sincerely that 'the gravitation of sensible bodies towards the centre of the earth must be produced by the movement of some fluid . . .' And he went on, 'A body is never moved naturally except by another body which impels it by touching it.' Reliance in this way upon the powers of reason was really a defect of Leibnitz's science. He was no experimentalist. Writing to Samuel Clarke he once said, 'When I was a young man I also was inclined to believe in atoms and the void; but reason brought me back.'

Leibnitz was familiar with the work of the English men of

science as well as that of French scientists, because he visited London and met Boyle and other members of the Royal Society. He seems never to have adopted the 'experimental philosophy', however, and when Leibnitz became famous it was for his philosophical writings and his discovery of the differential calculus. By 1676, when he became librarian to the Duke of Brunswick, Leibnitz had advanced a long way and was employing the calculus after discovering it independently, so far as is known, of Newton. Although he was so versatile a genius he was one of the least appreciated men of the time. He died in 1716 and was buried, according to an eye-witness, 'more like a robber than what he really was, the ornament of his country'.

Leibnitz followed deliberately the tradition of Bacon and was convinced of the value of scientific research. He saw, too, the great ignorance of the human race which, he remarked, 'in relation to the sciences which minister to our happiness, appears to me like a disorderly rabble marching in the darkness'. There was also a practical bias in his plans: 'The value and even the mark of true science consists in my opinion in the useful inventions which can be derived from it.' Remarks like these do not, however, reveal the whole of Leibnitz's point of view. In practice he was impatient of Newton's experimental philosophy. Looking back on the period of Leibnitz's writings the Scottish mathematician Maclaurin explained that Newton 'used to call his philosophy *experimental philosophy*, intimating by the name, the essential difference there is betwixt it and those systems which are the product of genius and invention only'. Maclaurin was thinking of Spinoza when he wrote of those who 'have lost themselves in the dark schemes of an inviolable and universal necessity', but he was thinking of Leibnitz when he added to his condemnation 'those who are ever dreaming themselves possest of the eternal reasons and primary causes of things'.

For Leibnitz's writings belong in the main to the class of *a priori* philosophy rather than to science. Without wishing to associate himself in the least with Descartes he really sought to revive the Cartesian tradition against which the experimental philosophy was a protest. Descartes and Leibnitz both claimed to explain the universe more by intuition than by a study of a vast amount of scientific evidence. For these two writers truth was rather a matter of acute thinking such as is required in mathematics. They attributed little importance to those innumerable facts which can be discovered only by experiment, or else ignored them altogether. Thus these two philosophers represent the rationalist school of thought while the men of science were of course empiricists. The separation of these two schools of thought was really equivalent at this time to the separation of science from philosophy.

It is not enough, however, to dismiss Leibnitz's writings as representing a failure to understand the true nature of science. Leibnitz represents, rather, a portent of that philosophical criticism of science which the empiricists could not in the end avoid altogether and which indeed becomes desirable at a late stage in the more developed sciences. Leibnitz was by no means simply a philosopher who could not understand Newton's *Principia.* On the contrary he understood this great work so well that he felt it necessary to examine the philosophical assumptions which were implicit in it. Unfortunately he went farther and set himself the task of remedying what he considered were the defects in Newton's scheme. Leibnitz's conception of a law of nature was unacceptable to men of science. He began, as did Descartes, with the activity of a Creator, and like Descartes also he propounded a theory that the universe is a perfect mechanism which once set going needed no intervention by the Deity to regulate its movements. By introducing the argument that God must have created the best of all possible worlds Leibnitz introduced the complication of moral values and laid himself open to the ridicule which Voltaire heaped upon him in *Candide.* It is extremely interesting to see that Leibnitz tried to escape from the doctrine of mechanical necessity by supposing that the laws of nature are an expression of a pre-established harmony. His theory of *monads* may be regarded as an answer to the Epicureans of his time. According to Leibnitz the fundamental entities of the universe are not atoms but monads; these resemble atoms but each has a soul and is self-determining within the limitations of his theory that there is a 'pre-established' harmony in the world. Voltaire had little patience with these subtleties. 'A Frenchman who comes to London finds great differences in philosophy as he does in other matters,' he wrote. 'In Paris the universe is supposed to consist of vortices of subtle matter; in London these do not exist. With us it is the pressure of the [vortex of the] moon which causes the tides; the English think that the sea gravitates towards the moon. . . . Light, for a Cartesian is something in the air; for a Newtonian it comes from the sun in six and a half minutes. . . .' Voltaire gave a bitter and exaggerated account of the intolerance which drove Descartes out of the country and led to his death at Stockholm and compared it with the reverence the English felt for Newton. Newton's theory of gravitation was 'sublime', the vortex theory was full of occult notions.

In 1735–6 the Académie Royale des Sciences sent out two expeditions to obtain conclusive evidence for the flattening of the earth. Both Huygens and Newton had believed the earth was flattened towards the poles but they differed widely in their estimates. Begun by J. D. Cassini (1652–1712), one of the greatest of the astronomers associated with the Paris observatory in its early years, the study of the shape of the earth was at first carried on by measuring the length of a pendulum which beat seconds at points of known latitude on the earth's surface. Cassini's son Jacques continued his father's work and in his book *De la grandeur et de la figure de la Terre* he concluded that the earth is elongated rather than flattened at the poles. This was a conclusion exactly opposite to that of Newton and Huygens and a lively dispute broke out which had as sequel these expeditions of the French academy. Louis XV gave his support to the venture and funds were provided by the government. Maupertuis, Clairaut and Le Monnier were members of the party which went to the north and worked in Lapland, while La Condamine, Bouguer and Godin were in the party which undertook the very exacting work nearer the equator in Peru. The evidence obtained provided support for the Newtonian theory that there is a flattening at the poles. Maupertuis, who was the chief critic of Cassini, triumphed immoderately when the results came out. The most important work produced as a result of these expeditions was Clairaut's theoretical study of the form of the earth. This work (*Théorie de la Figure de la Terre,* 1743) disposed of the differences between Newton's and Huygens's estimates.

There was a group of exceedingly able mathematicians in Europe during the later part of the eighteenth century: Clairaut, Euler, Lagrange and Laplace to name those best known for their work on celestial mechanics. Analytical methods—the methods of Cartesian algebra, combined with the calculus of Newton and Leibnitz—almost completely replaced the tedious methods of geometry used by Huygens and Newton although these continued to be used in England by slavish adherents to the *Principia*. Not only were the new methods far more expeditious, they were also far more general and they were suited to deal with quantities such as energy and potential which were practically beyond the reach of geometry. The more general nature of the solutions meant that the treatment of special cases could be quickly deduced instead of being treated from first principles. Lagrange completed the work of Huygens on the conservation of energy. His *Mécanique Analytique* of 1788 set the tone of modern physical treatises. The treatment of problems was almost entirely mathematical and there is little reference to the physical processes discussed. With Lagrange there is little opportunity for picturing what is supposed to be taking place. Instead, much use is made of theoretical conceptions which are themselves mathematically defined. For example, in seeking to discover in what direction a change in a given system will take place under the action of the forces present in it, Lagrange made use of the conception of *potential*. This conception really enabled Lagrange to make good the deficiencies of a law of conservation of kinetic energy which has in fact very little application in that form. In the example of

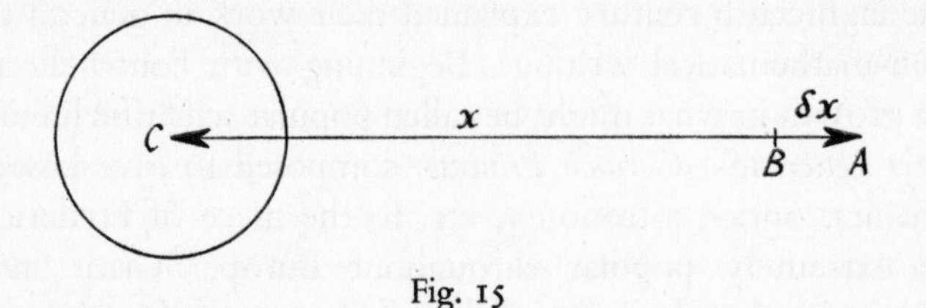

Fig. 15

the gravitational field around a large spherical mass the potential at any point is the work which would be obtained by bringing unit mass from an infinite distance up to that point. At any distance x away from the centre of the sphere (Fig. 15) there will be a force F acting on the unit mass and for any small movement δx towards the sphere an amount of work (or energy) $F. \delta x$ will be obtained. This is the change of potential from A to B (written V) and it follows that since

$$\delta V = - F. \delta x$$

$$F = - \frac{\delta V}{\delta x}$$

or rather, from the principles of the calculus,

$$F = - \frac{dV}{dx}$$

This gives the well-known relation between force and potential in a gravitational field. Students of physics will be aware how much this method is used in other subjects, notably magnetism and electrostatics.

Newtonian physics is no doubt easier to follow with the aid of models or pictorial representations than the physics of Lagrange. Analytical methods indeed make diagrams largely unnecessary and there may be objections to the representation of the steps of an argument in pictorial manner. Laplace, the great contemporary of Lagrange, frequently omitted some of the steps of his argument and simply wrote 'it is quite easy to see . . . etc.' though this was not always quite true. It might be imagined that the technical works produced by scientists at this time would be found to be of such a nature that popular interest declined. Yet this does not seem to have happened. Several of the great scientists of the eighteenth century explained their work in general terms in non-mathematical writings. Beginning with Fontenelle there was a growth in what might be called popular scientific literature. Euler's *Letters to a German Princess,* composed to give lessons in mechanics, optics, astronomy, etc. to the niece of Frederick II, were extremely popular throughout Europe. Great interest was also stirred up by some of the achievements of Lagrange and Laplace, who succeeded with their analytical methods in solving some of the great questions of the age. It will be convenient therefore to say briefly what these problems were.

Although excluded by the official ruling of the Catholic Church until 1822 the Copernican system was generally accepted by educated people during the eighteenth century. The planets go round the sun in elliptical orbits which have the sun at one focus of the ellipse. The planets are also rotating at speeds which could in certain cases be determined by observing spots on their surfaces. This rotation caused a flattening of the shape so that it was no longer spherical. In the seventeenth century Robert Hooke explained this by saying that a planet was 'somewhat of the shape of a turnip' or, he added, 'a solid made by an ellipsis turned round upon its shorter diameter'. The moon remained something of a special problem, however, for this satellite revolves around the earth and rotates at such a rate that the whole of the other hemisphere is never seen. Using the principles of the Aristotelians or the argument that this is the best of all possible worlds some kind of explanation had been given for the phenomenon. It seemed to Laplace and Lagrange extremely improbable that the moon's spin had become adjusted by accident.

Lagrange's explanation may be given as follows. The moon, having solidified, as he supposed, in the gravitational field of the earth, its shape is not that of a sphere or a spheroid with a circular equator, it is lozenge shaped. Consequently it might be shown that the moon possessed a minimum potential energy when its longest axis pointed towards the earth. Any slight displacement would cause oscillations like those of a magnet needle. A sort of tidal action on the solid moon had brought about the standard rate of rotation which keeps the same side (approximately) turned towards the earth.

Far more important than this problem, however, was the problem of the stability or otherwise of the solar system. Newton suggested that the system of the planets revolving about the sun in ellipses might not be stable and might require some intervention from the Deity from time to time to regulate the movements. Newton left out of account the gravitational influences of the planets on each other. Although it could be seen immediately that such influences would be small there were no grounds for saying that in time large disturbances might not accumulate. There was little faith at this time in the interest the Deity might show in the fortunes of the planets, and it was realized that life on the earth was possible as a result of conditions which were quite delicately adjusted.

The history of this problem begins with the studies of comets made by Edmund Halley in the seventeenth century. These bodies are especially interesting in that their paths appeared to exhibit the effects of gravitational disturbances or perturbations on quite a large scale. From a study of the records Halley was of the opinion that the comets of 1531, 1607 and 1682 were in reality successive appearances of one and the same comet. The difficulty in the theory, which otherwise accorded with the Newtonian system, was that the two intervals, of seventy-six and seventy-five years, were not equal. The difference was actually nearer two years than one. Was such a disturbance in the path of the planet (and thus its period) the result of powerful gravitational forces due to the larger planets near which the comet had passed on its longer journey? As the French scientist Arago later remarked. 'The answer to this question would introduce comets into the category of ordinary planets or would exclude them for ever.'

The necessary mathematical method for dealing with the complex problem in gravitation, where two gravitational fields are considered simultaneously, was worked out in a form of approximation by Clairaut. During the year 1758 Clairaut undertook to predict when the comet of 1682 would reappear and almost exactly whereabouts in the heavens it would first be seen. He estimated that Jupiter would cause a retardation of 518 days in the period of the comet and Saturn a further 100 days, giving a total of more than a year and eight months. It was said by Arago with some exaggeration that the sporting interests of the human race were so aroused by Clairaut's predictions that more than a thousand telescopes were nightly in use to follow the comet after its first appearance on the night it was expected. The orbit was just what Clairaut said it would be. Such great perturbations could not, nevertheless, be accepted calmly. They posed the question whether the entire solar system is fundamentally unstable in its present state. Beginning in 1773 Laplace devoted many years of his life to this great problem.

Laplace was the son of humble parents and very little is known of his early years, which were spent at Beaumont-en-Auge, a small French country town. His origins have a certain resemblance with those of Newton. Laplace was, however, more concerned to rise in the social scale than was Newton. By 1767 he was in Paris, where he had gone to seek his fortune, trusting entirely to his mathematical powers. Lacking a wealthy patron Laplace decided to approach the mathematician D'Alembert who was then principally taken up with his work as an editor of the Encyclopedia. Now D'Alembert's origins were also obscure, but he was not accustomed on this account to give interviews to unknown and poor young men. He resisted Laplace's importunity until the latter sent him a letter on the general principles of mechanics. This gained him D'Alembert's support and interest and from that date Laplace's fortunes were assured. He was appointed immediately to a professorship at the Paris Military School. Laplace was indeed a striking example of innate mathematical genius and he was fortunate in that this was perceived by D'Alembert.

Unfortunately Laplace was inclined to be unscrupulous both in his scientific writings and in his public career. He never hesitated to take the ideas of others without acknowledgement. Thus he used the conception of potential in his publications without reference to Lagrange. Politically he must be judged in relation to the dangers of the times. Even so he was unduly pliable. With the increase in Napoleon's power Laplace abandoned his republican principles and gained from Napoleon the post of Minister of the Interior. It did not take Napoleon long to see that he had made a mistake. Laplace was removed after five or six weeks and raised to the Senate. When, by 1814, it had become clear that Napoleon's empire was at an end, Laplace hastened to pay his respects to the Bourbons, and he became a marquis on their restoration. Nevertheless, none of this can detract from the greatness of his *Mécanique Céleste*—the next great landmark after Newton's *Principia* in the history of theoretical astronomy.

The *Mécanique Céleste* is highly technical; indeed Laplace wrote another work to explain his ideas in general terms. This work, the *Système du Monde,* is in some ways a more satisfactory production. Certainly for the historian it gives a most useful account of the progress of theoretical astronomy at that time. It was translated into English and widely read as an accompaniment to the progress of observational astronomy at the end of the eighteenth century. The chief contribution of Laplace was the demonstration that the solar system is not unstable as had been feared.

Writing of the laws of Nature in the *Système du Monde*, Laplace says, 'It is to discover these laws and to reduce them to the least possible number, that all our efforts should tend; for the first causes, and the intimate nature of beings, will be to us eternally unknown.' This interest in reducing the number of laws of Nature is an interesting feature of eighteenth-century science and represents, no doubt, a special quality of Laplace's mind. Of the law of universal gravitation which he may have envied Newton for discovering, Laplace says: 'We shall see that this great law of Nature represents all the celestial phenomena even in their minutest details, that there is not one single inequality of their motions which is not derived from it, with the most admirable precision.'

As Arago explained, Laplace showed 'that the planetary ellipses are perpetually variable; that the extremities of their major axes make the tour of the heavens; that independently of an oscillatory motion, the planes of their orbits experience a displacement in virtue of which their intersections with the plane of the terrestrial orbit are each year directed towards different stars.' 'In the midst of this apparent chaos there is one element which remains constant, or is merely subject to small periodic changes: namely, the major axis of each orbit. . . .' There were, however, some troublesome facts about the periods of Jupiter and Saturn, for the former appeared to be increasing its period while the latter was decreasing (when the modern observations were compared with those of ancient times). In the Newtonian system this could only mean that Jupiter was spiralling towards the sun while Saturn was spiralling away. Euler and Lagrange, however, showed that these changes were not unidirectional; they were periodic and varied back and forth over a period of centuries.

'I have succeeded in demonstrating', wrote Laplace, 'that whatever be the masses of the planets, in as much as they all move in the same direction, in orbits of small eccentricity, and little inclined to each other; their secular inequalities will be periodic, and contained within narrow limits, so that the planetary system will only oscillate about a mean state, from which it will deviate but by a very small quantity. . . .' Affected perhaps by *les philosophes* who stressed the value and power of scientific knowledge, Laplace adopted a tone of confidence in his writings which was a new thing in science. His remark that God is an unnecessary hypothesis in theoretical studies of the solar system is well known. So also is his statement of the determinism of events, which, he said, was so complete that the course of the entire universe could be foretold by a sufficiently great mathematician, given the initial state of things.

How, granted the law of universal gravity, had the solar system come into existence? The answer given by Laplace was the celebrated nebular hypothesis, which has not received support from subsequent investigators. According to this theory—which was propounded in a somewhat similar form a little earlier by the philosopher Kant—the sun was originally the centre of an immense nebula. This nebula was at a very high temperature and consisted of a disc-shaped mass of gas or vapour in a state of rotation. No planets at first existed. Through radiation of energy the nebula gradually cooled and experienced consequently a gradual condensation under mutual gravitation of its parts. This increased the rate of rotation so as to maintain a constant angular momentum. Laplace considered that at this point rings of more condensed matter would separate so that a series of concentric whorls or rings would be formed. Any irregularity in the density of the ring could then account, in time, for the absorption of all this matter in a given ring in one single body. Thus we get a series of planets. Their satellites could be accounted for by a more detailed consideration of the rotating masses which first 'solidified' out. This theory was in vogue for about a hundred years and was finally given up because it was shown that such an evolutionary process as Laplace imagined could not have taken place on the relatively small scale of the solar system. On the other hand there was evidence that what he described had taken place in the breakdown of the great nebulae in the birth of stars.

The exceptionally theoretical work of Laplace and others was counterbalanced during the eighteenth century by some important observational work by Bradley in the first half of the century and by William Herschel towards its end. This was the chief

English contribution. Bradley set out to detect the parallactic movements among the stars which must result from the earth's motion in its orbit. This chief requirement of the Copernican system had never been satisfied and it defeated Bradley also. He discovered instead an effect called the aberration of light (1729), a phenomenon which results from the motion of the earth just as infallibly as the parallax should do. This phenomenon, which is an outcome of relative motion, was suggested to Bradley by his observation of a weather vane on a ship's mast when he was sailing on the Thames. It provided the explanation of the curious shifts in the star positions which he had detected with great delicacy of observation over a period of three years or so. Bradley also discovered a *nutation* or 'nodding' of the pole which, instead of tracing out a circle in the heavens as is required to explain precession, traces instead a wavy curve. The irregularity was due to the moon's gravity.

By the end of the century the sweep of the law of gravitation was seen to be enormous. It had to be admitted that Laplace was right: all the effects of nature were almost certainly due to only a few grand universal laws. The determination of the mass of the earth by Maskelyne in 1774 and by Cavendish in 1797–8 gave the value of the Newtonian constant G through which it proved to be possible to calculate the masses of other planets and, later, of certain binary stars. By the time William Herschel was ready to begin his epoch-making observations the human mind was ready for this new venture; it had, it seemed, comprehended the solar system down to its quite small details and now it asked the question: what of the stars?

CHAPTER SIX

From Locke to Voltaire

It is an interesting and significant fact that scientific work does not produce its greatest imaginative effects at first hand. More than any other human activity it requires its interpreters, not for the purpose of translating scientific work into merely popular form, but to help determine what philosophical significance, if any, there may be in the science of an age. There can be no denying that this broad general influence of science has been, and will continue to be, of very great importance. The results of research are thus always human quite as much as they are technical or technological.

In fact we may well discern two types of effect which flow from the advance of science. For, firstly, the world of ideas may be stirred by the intellectual gains that are made; while secondly people's way of living and even their general beliefs may be powerfully affected by large-scale applications of knowledge which, as we have seen so well in the past hundred years, transform the human environment. The first of these effects might be called philosophical, while the second is largely psychological and concerns much larger numbers of people. Many more people appear to be impressed with the power of science because of its part in the production of jet planes and atomic bombs than are concerned to think about the implications of such new advances in science as have come under the general headings of relativity or quantum mechanics. Yet the philosophical results of new knowledge may easily prove of greater moment to the world than any number of new inventions.

The Newtonian epoch taught all educated men—a small minority—the importance of scientific law. This lesson still needs to be learned. The success of all science depends upon the ability we have to frame valid scientific laws and arrive at fruitful abstract conceptions. Without this science would be purely descriptive or classificatory. From John Locke to Voltaire is much the same period as from Huygens and Newton to Laplace, so that this chapter proceeds parallel, and is not chronologically subsequent, to the one that went before. All the same the subject matter is very different. The philosophers and writers with whom we are concerned were with the exception of Leibnitz, neither mathematicians nor men of science. Their writings had great influence, greater one would say than those of the men of science themselves. To a large extent these philosophers did not fully understand the science of their age and occupied themselves only transiently with it. But they grasped certain points with firmness, and science reacted on them producing a distinct result in their thinking. Then through them and the books they wrote a whole age was moved in a new direction. But it was certainly a direction that was the result indirectly of scientific inquiry.

Going beyond this point is difficult. But we should be blind if we did not see how much economic and political change depends upon men's beliefs. The whole structure of the modern world has been affected by the science of the seventeenth and eighteenth centuries and it is only because the chains of cause and effect have been obscure that no historian has ever worked them out in detail. A. N. Whitehead, however, saw the Newtonian synthesis as the beginning of the modern world and his words may be quoted as the introduction to this chapter. Writing of Galileo and Newton in his *Essays in Science and Philosophy,* he remarked: 'Think for a moment of the possible course of history supposing that the life's work of these two men were absent. At the commencement of the eighteenth century many curious and baffling facts of physical science would have been observed, vaguely connected by detached and obscure hypotheses. But in the absence of a clear physical synthesis, with its overwhelming success in the solution of problems which from the most remote antiquity had excited attention, the motive for the next advance would have been absent. All epochs pass, and the scientific ferment of the seventeenth century would have died down. Locke's philosophy would never have been written; and Voltaire when he visited England would have carried back to France merely a story of expanding commerce and of the political rivalries between aristocratic factions. Europe might then have lacked the French intellectual movement. But the Fates do not always offer the same gifts twice, and it is possible that the eighteenth century might then have prepared for the western races an intellectual sleep of a thousand years, prosperous with the quiet slow exploitation of the American continent, as manual labour slowly subdued its rivers, its forests, and its prairies. I am not concerned to deny that the result might have been happier, for the chariot of Phoebus is a dangerous vehicle. My only immediate thesis is that it would have been very different.'

Since those words were written the chariot of Phoebus has continued on its dangerous career. We have had a Second World War and all the new military technology connected with nuclear weapons. Many might after all prefer an intellectual sleep of a thousand years, but it is not to be had. The question to be asked is what was so arresting about Locke's philosophy and Voltaire's influence that this noted writer refers to them as being so decisive? Both were concerned in some way with the Newtonian synthesis but in what way, we may ask, and how were Locke and Voltaire so influential?

John Locke (1632–1704) was only a schoolboy when the first major political event of his life, the execution of Charles I, took place in 1649. By circumstance he was well placed as an observer of the changes that followed, especially since, after 1666, he was confidential secretary and a personal friend of Lord Ashley, First Earl of Shaftesbury. Shaftesbury's activities must have brought Locke many experiences: the political and religious struggles of the age were the cause of his spending the years 1675–9 in France, while in 1683 he had to follow Shaftesbury to Holland. In 1688, the year which ended half a century of political struggle, Locke returned to England. In 1690 he published his famous work entitled *Essay Concerning Human Understanding*.

The story behind this book is that Locke held a reunion of some of his friends when he was secretary to Lord Ashley, at Exeter House, and that their discussion of political and theological problems led them to realize the need of a general philosophical inquiry. This Locke undertook to carry out, but owing to the disturbances of the time and the difficulties in the problem the work occupied him for many years. It is indeed remarkable that such troubled times produced a work of this nature, for it is Locke's chief characteristic that he stresses how our beliefs derive from our experiences and can be understood in this light. The book has great significance for the main tradition of English life for Locke presents in it the justification of the right, as he saw it, of the individual thinker to follow freely the findings of his experience. So far as the men of science were concerned, however, Locke was an innovator because he championed a theory about human knowledge which had been unpopular ever since the time of Plato and because he succeeded in reversing the whole situation. So that after Locke it was Plato's tradition that was defeated and discredited while Locke's opinions received increasing acceptance both in England and on the Continent. It remains to be said what these opinions were.

Briefly Locke believed that all ideas come from human experience and none are possessed by the mind without such experience. Ideas cannot, that is, be 'innate' as Plato, Descartes and others had maintained. Mathematics had seemed to many thinkers to be evidence that we have certain ideas independently of experience, and Plato went so far so to throw doubts on the reliability of our senses as a guide to true knowledge. In the seventeenth century the argument from mathematics was not so convincing, possibly because of the part that observation and experiment were playing in the studies of the scientific societies. Locke was at Oxford for fifteen years after 1652, and during this time the new experimental science became influential in the university. Locke is really one of the first philosophers who allowed for this type of inquiry, and his belief that there are certain primary qualities belonging to bodies, such as their bulk, situation, motion or rest, falls into line with the teaching of Galileo.

Locke did not consider himself to be a scientist. 'The commonwealth of learning is not at this time without master-builders whose mighty designs, in advancing the sciences, will leave lasting monuments to the admiration of posterity,' he wrote, 'but every one must not hope to be a Boyle or a Sydenham; and in an age that produces such masters as the great Huygenius and the incomparable Mr. Newton, with some others of that strain, it is ambition enough to be employed as an under-labourer in clearing the ground a little, and removing some of the rubbish that lies in the way to knowledge. . . .'

He thought it was clear enough that the primary qualities of bodies really belong to them and are inseparable from them. The secondary qualities are however purely subjective and arise only in the mind of the person who is aware of them. Without the eye there would be no colours, without the ear no sounds, and so on. Physics for long proceeded on this basis. Measurable quantities like mass or momentum provide the basis, and the aim is to extend measurement as far as possible, even colour in time being replaced by the wave-lengths of the light that is used in an experiment. An objective world of primary qualities, therefore, exists and gives rise through our perceptions to all the other qualities which are thus purely mental.[1] In fact this distinction proves on examination to be far less sound than it appeared to men like Locke in the seventeenth century. It was, however, part of a general theory in which, according to Locke, the mind begins as a blank sheet and receives impressions which are ideas produced by the objects in the external world. As such it has remained what we may call the common-sense view ever since. In England, certainly, the notion of innate ideas, whereby the mind is naturally equipped to deal with certain kinds of relationship, such as we have in mathematics, has never been as prominent as it has been in France owing to the influence of Descartes. But even in France Locke's *Essay Concerning Human Understanding* was widely read in spite of Descartes's influence there. Bertrand Russell remarks on this in his *History of Western Philosophy*: 'Quite illogically, the victory of Locke's philosophy in England and France was largely due to the prestige of Newton. Descartes's authority as a philosopher was enhanced, in his own day, by his work in mathematics and natural philosophy. But his doctrine of vortices was definitely inferior to Newton's law of gravitation as an explanation of the solar system. The victory of the Newtonian cosmogony diminished men's respect for Descartes and increased their respect for England.' The originality of Locke lay in his working out of an exposition of a point of view that fitted on well to the new natural

[1]Locke's consideration of the part played by 'reflection' is necessarily omitted from this review.

science of the age. This part of Locke's work met the needs of the time just as fortunately as did those parts of his *Essay* which dealt with moral and political problems.

Above all the *Essay* took the first steps that any writer of breadth had taken in placing man in a naturalistic setting. Locke denied that man has any specially privileged place in creation or that God's purposes were all directed towards satisfying his needs. He showed, so far as he could, that the functioning of the mind can be understood in this context. Our knowledge is certainly not divinely implanted in us. On the contrary it owes nearly everything to experience. A man is not born with a key to the meaning of the world; he must discover what he can even though there may be strict limits to the success of the endeavour. He suspected, he said, that '*natural philosophy is not capable of being made a science*' (his own italics) and he preferred to consider our natural capacities lay rather in the direction of morals 'that sort of knowledge which is most suited to our natural capacities, and carries with it our greatest interest'. He would not, he added, 'be thought to disesteem or dissuade the study of *nature*. . . . All that I would say is, that we should not be too forwardly possessed with the opinion or expectation of knowledge where it is not to be had, or by ways that will not attain to it: that we should not take doubtful systems for complete sciences; nor unintelligible notions for scientific demonstrations.'

It has always seemed strange that Locke was so sceptical about the possibilities of physics, only a few years after the publication of Newton's *Principia*. Very probably his attitude had the effect of discouraging ambitious cosmic speculation and of reconciling people to their traditional religious teachings. Without this moderating influence the questions raised by natural science point to a conflict with much that was part of traditional theology, but this conflict was postponed until the middle of the eighteenth century. The philosopher Thomas Hobbes, who belongs to an earlier period than Locke, was chiefly responsible in England for this extreme kind of materialistic philosophy, based on a grasp of the work of Galileo, Descartes and others, which Locke obviously disliked. Indeed most men of science in the mid-seventeenth century in England denied at one time or another that they were

'Hobbists', Newton among them. Hobbes's philosophy denied that there was anything but matter in the world, even mind being a kind of matter. This was so destructive of any spiritual or moral view of life or even of experience that it was considered extremely atheistical. And in a serious Puritan age this was most objectionable. The persistence of a religious view which placed restrictions on all scientific explanations lasted at least until after Newton's death in 1727.

But the popularization of science was already falling into other hands. Professor Butterfield in his book *The Origins of Modern Science* considered that the French writer Fontenelle was 'the most important single link between the scientific revolution and the *philosophe* movement'. By the *philosophe* movement it needs to be explained that he meant that extremely important activity in literature which came from a number of kindred spirits in France in the eighteenth century and which gave us as an outcome not merely the articles in Diderot's *Encyclopedia,* but a new world view, rationalistic, anti-clerical and receptive to all new scientific ideas. This movement more than anything else has led to the continuous undermining of the authority of the churches and of the intellectual claims of religion in the modern world. Fontenelle was secretary of the Académie Royale des Sciences from 1699 to 1741. He was a literary man who turned his mind to science and he has preserved for us evidence of the increasing interest of his age for all matters scientific. The popular audience was increasing both in France and England and such a book as Fontenelle's *Plurality of Worlds* which was pure popularized and imaginative astronomy was received with acclamation. 'He did not merely popularize the scientific achievement of the seventeenth century,' says Butterfield. 'It is important to note that the literary man intervenes at this crucial stage of the story and performs a second function—the translation of the scientific achievement into a new view of life and the universe.'

The new view which was created by the writers we have to consider was above all secular. Professor Butterfield describes it as a 'colossal secularization'. It was by no means entirely the product of the new physical science, because many were far more interested in natural history; and natural history, much of it very undistinguished, fills many pages of the scientific journals. Also geographical exploration and the increasing importance attached to supplies of raw materials were helping to arouse men's imaginations so that science fell into place as part of a programme for altering and advancing civilization through deliberate effort.

It is surprising to realize the extent to which the Newtonian point of view triumphed on the Continent over the teaching of Descartes. For Descartes was at first extremely influential. 'It was in England and Holland', says Daniel Mornet (*The European Inheritance*, Vol. II, Oxford), 'that the victory was won . . . it was Newton's fame, and the teaching and writings of his Dutch disciples, that finally defeated and routed Cartesian rationalism in the field of the natural sciences. Everyone, in short, became Newtonian, not only in the Royal Society, of which he was the president, but also outside it. But it was mainly through Dutch scholars, teaching in the universities, that the Newtonian method gained its hold on European thought.' The scientists referred to were principally Gravesande, Desaguliers (who was also an engineer), and Musschenbroek. What these men stood for principally was a complete severance of experimental science, which should be given mathematical treatment, from all forms of general philosophy. Speculative systems were at an end. The only sane philosophical outlook that could be tolerated was that expressed by John Locke, whose *Essay* was read on the Continent quite as much as it was read in England.

How big a blow Locke's *Essay* was for the more ambitious schemes which thinkers had entertained and still entertained it is difficult now to imagine. Locke's empiricism, his limited expectation and his readiness for a tentative conclusion have entered into our habits of thought so that what he says seems almost to be commonplace. We need to compare him with such a writer as Leibnitz (1646–1716) to see what he really means in the history of thought. For Leibnitz was by no means satisfied with the limitations Locke set on the operations of the human mind. He provides, by comparison, an example of that 'quest for certainty' which John Dewey has described as a predisposition of the entire classic tradition. Experimental science could never answer all the big questions; it could be doubted if it could 'teach anything universally' as Hobbes put it. It had its uses, no doubt, but the exercise of the reason appeared the only way to arrive at that certainty which men desired and which Leibnitz considered could be attained. So it is that at the height of the new scientific movement we find Leibnitz going back to the old tradition and arguing that 'the meditations of the theologians and of the philosophers known as Schoolmen are not wholly to be despised'. Reason, not experiment and observation, alone was capable 'of setting up rules which are certain'; physical contingent fact instead of being the beginning of knowledge ought, as Leibnitz thought, on the contrary to be derived from eternal metaphysical truths. The cause of the universe, it was self-evident, must be 'the ends of God'. Leibnitz believed the Newtonian analysis was in the last resort an impious explanation, a confusion of the natural with the artificial; it was also erroneous in its foundation on the conception of absolute time and space. Leibnitz seems to have come to the conclusion that since no mechanism for some of the laws of mechanics could be imagined there was really a breakdown in the ordinary cause-effect relationship. He ascribed such laws to God's choice of them for their fitness.

As a philosopher Leibnitz really stands for the reinstating of the theories which Locke had driven out. Necessary truths, he said, 'such as we find in mathematics, and particularly in arithmetic and geometry, must have principles the proof of which does not depend upon examples, nor consequently upon the senses, although without the senses one would never have thought of them. So also logic, metaphysics, and morals are full of such truths, and consequently their proofs can only come from those internal principles which are called *innate*.' Possibly because he was a mathematician and Locke was not, Leibnitz would not abandon his belief in innate ideas. The struggle was no mere minor academic one, but should be seen as quite as important as the struggle between the nominalists and the realists of centuries before. Once again it was Plato's philosophy that occasioned the dispute, for the belief in innate ideas goes back to him just as does the doctrine that reality inheres in the ideal forms and not in the objects of sense. On both questions the scientific movement depended on the defeat of Platonism, and today, it seems true to say, no philosophy or system of ideas is less convincing than the metaphysics so persuasively presented in the Platonic dialogues. There is more than one reason for the decline of the classics in our civilization, but one of them is that many of the ideas which were so long respected and held in something like awe are now felt to be antiquated, irrelevant or meaningless.

How Leibnitz tried to save men from thinking of nature as the men of science of his time were coming to think of it, how he tried to preserve that sense of a purpose in events which it is now so difficult to recapture, can be described only by giving an account of Leibnitz's philosophy, of his argument that this is the best of all the possible worlds that might have been created, and of his principle of sufficient reason. The quarrel between him and Locke is now regarded as a matter for the text-books of philosophy and the chief influence Leibnitz has had, it might be said, has been in the writings of philosophers like Whitehead who have kept alive the criticism of science as a scheme for the explanation of nature. In reality the problem at issue is of perennial importance, for it goes to the heart of what we mean by 'explaining' nature, and the fact that Leibnitz's arguments are forgotten results not so much from the fact that they were disproved on any fundamental grounds as from our disinclination for the religious type of explanation he put forward and our acceptance of scientific relationships. Leibnitz's case was weakened historically by his failure to grasp the new treatment of Newton's *Principia*; on the other side it has to be said that he refused to ignore the metaphysical problems which Newtonian science produced, and that some such method as he adopted for clothing the bare relationships of science can still be considered as a possibility. Leibnitz illustrates extremely well the important fact that explanation is always relative to the purposes and assumptions which are involved. He was aware, as few were at that time, of the inadequacy of purely mechanical explanations of natural phenomena. But inadequate for what? Not, it must be confessed, for the purpose of calculation and prediction: Laplace as we have seen showed that this was not so. The inadequacy, if it had to be admitted at all, was on the side of all these questions which men desire to answer when they compare their lives and emotions with the apparently impersonal and remote operations of the external world.

The curious thing is that, however exalted Leibnitz's aims may really have been, his antagonists, who were chiefly among the English writers, condemned him for his impiety in dreaming himself possessed 'of the eternal reasons and primary causes of things'. A generation which had read Locke and revered Newton could not accept Leibnitz's argument that the laws of nature were an expression of the pre-established harmony which God had imposed on things. English thought had passed through a period of difficulty but was then in view of a more optimistic interpretation. At first there had been uncertainty why, within the Christian framework of ideas, God had made the world he had—far vaster than formerly imagined and certainly more curious and unexpected. It might be that the world was only a ruin of what it had been in the time of its perfection and that all the repellent and frightening aspects of nature were the result of man's sin. Newton, however, represented a far more confident outlook, for he argued that science indicated God's mode of constructing the universe and even his constant attention to its manner of going. Although the English set going the powerful belief that the universe can be understood in natural terms they showed a readiness to accept man's relative insignificance in the scheme of things. Man must not set himself up in rebellion, argued Pope but must *accept,*

> 'Or meteor-like, flame lawless through the void,
> Destroying others, by himself destroy'd.'

Christianity might be widely discredited, but there was a natural religion, an argument from nature to God, which gave reassurance in a changing world.

How the natural religion of some of the English writers and their belief in tolerance and enlightenment, as opposed to bigotry and superstition, spread to France through the writings of Voltaire is an interesting story. What Voltaire did was to ridicule the Cartesian philosophy which still survived in France and bring to the notice of his countrymen (1728) the enormous success of Newtonian principles, and still more, to represent the former as obscure and erroneous while the latter was clear for any intelligent man to check for himself. Newtonianism was the truth, Cartesianism was all imagination. The sarcastic way in which Voltaire upset the surviving Cartesian notions and the way he attacked clericalism as an institution for the maintenance of superstitions no doubt explains how the atmosphere which science generated in France was more bitter than in England. Advancing secular knowledge, Voltaire's revolutionary teachings as to what constituted the important events of history and who were the benefactors of the human race, above all the notion, in France as in England, that enlightened human nature could be trusted in place of old authorities, were some of the conditions which produced the revolutionary spirit of the time. A change of outlook which had to some extent been delayed through the estrangement of the English and the French and the survival of a vigorous Cartesian philosophy had to take place in France, and the social and political conditions were such as to provoke a heightened sense of rapid and revolutionary change. Even Voltaire was soon outclassed in the vigour of his speculations—'he was bigoted, he believed in a God', and an atheistical and materialistic school of thought arose which was much more extreme than any of the contemporary writers in England could dare to be.

What was new in the eighteenth century was the dominance of so wide a range of ideas by the conception of a natural order. The discovery of this order was possible; to defy it was folly. Popular interest in science was enormously increased and it became accepted that new scientific discoveries were things which could be discussed in polite society. The expeditions which were sent out, the books that were written about the earth and the universe, the new discoveries, the question whether other worlds existed—all these excited the minds of educated men and altered profoundly the literature of civilization. During the later part of the eighteenth century some of these problems were removed from the sphere of speculation and solved through the elaboration of new mathematical methods. In this the English were very much left behind as a result of their admiration of the *Principia*. Once having learnt to do away with unnecessary mechanisms the mathematical physicists of the Continent carried the theory of the solar system a good deal farther than Newton. As has been indicated they succeeded, moreover, in discovering ways of formulating physical relationships which were much more general than any used before.

For in the end it had to be realized that even Newton had brought into physics a number of ideas the validity of which was doubtful. They might even be superfluous. Absolute space and time have been in our own age quite abolished from the concepts of physics, and the notion of *force* is one which physics can logically dispense with altogether. These are rather technical points. The issue of the philosophical movement begun by Locke and continued in a more general way by Voltaire and the Encyclopedists, may be described as the defeat of Platonism and the setting up in its place of an empirical philosophy. So great a change naturally did not take place without a considerable convulsion in the intellectual world. In England many writers showed their hostility, and literature from the time of Swift onwards is full of this hostility or contempt. For it was clear to the writers that the empirical philosophy threatened the freedom of the mind to create by pure imagination its own empires. Turning aside from such difficult and frightening matters a whole host of writers sought to escape from philosophic despair into that world of nature which mathematical science left untouched. 'The discovery of the sciences of observation', writes Mornet, 'revealed, particularly in natural history, the complex and subtle secrets governing the processes of nature and particularly of life. . . . For instance, the *Spectacle de la Nature* by the Abbé Pluche (nine volumes from 1732 onwards; at least fifteen French editions; translations into English, Italian, and Spanish) extols in the last volume the goodness of God, who created the various shades of green in nature, so that our eyes might not be tired, and who invented tides, so that ships might be able to sail into harbour.'

These are precisely the sorts of statements that the scientific movement ruled out of court. Pope and Swift mocked at the scientists. Bishop Berkeley tried to show philosophically that materialism is unsound. But the victory undoubtedly lay with the rationalist thinkers who accepted science as an important positive advance from ignorance into enlightenment. A considerable school of philosophers continued to support Cartesianism—and Platonism—but their voices counted for less and less. By the end of the eighteenth century the Newtonian philosophy was supreme in a wider world than that of pure science.

There can be little doubt that the intervention of French writers such as D'Alembert, Diderot, Condorcet and above all of Voltaire contributed most to the victory of the scientific over the Cartesian, Platonic, or what survived of the Aristotelian point of view. Such a point of view in the age we are considering really represented the joining together of experimental science and mathematics. The famous French *Encyclopédie,* published between 1751 and 1780, was in all things a radical production, radical and critical in its treatment of moral and social problems, and stressing the importance of new knowledge. It was above all inspired by the scientific spirit. Denis Diderot, the principal editor, is remembered almost entirely for his participation in this great work. It was originally intended to prepare a translation of *Chambers's Encyclopaedia*, a British production, for the French market. A group of men, of whom Diderot, Condorcet and D'Alembert are the most famous, concluded that a totally new work was needed. With an astonishingly small group of helpers the new task was begun. The new *Encyclopedia* would be modern; it would challenge ancient authorities which were not yet superseded, it would be scientific; it would be French.

The chief burden of the work descended on the shoulders of Diderot. All the contributors soon became aware of the hostility they were arousing. As volume succeeded volume it was increasingly believed that they were not serving the cause of learning but were rather a band of conspirators who aimed to undermine the structure of society. Religiously and politically their views were especially unpopular and in 1759, after beginning in 1751, the publication of the *Encyclopedia* was prohibited by the Government. Some of the contributors, including the mathematician D'Alembert, then withdrew but Diderot continued the work. Because of lack of money, danger of arrest by the police and the need of secrecy, he was obliged to perform prodigies of work. For seven years he laboured on, writing hundreds of articles, collecting information, preparing notes, and in 1765 the last of the letterpress was issued. It was 1772 before the final volumes of the illustrations appeared.

Diderot is remembered as one who helped to provide the foundations of a new learning and a new liberalism. Through the *Encyclopedia* the stream of Newtonian science was directed into the main channel of European culture. It was not so much the facts as the general point of view of science that mattered, for there was in the articles a demand for evidence and fresh judgement. It had been possible for a European to be educated and remain ignorant of science. This could remain so no longer. The story is well known how the printer of Diderot's articles quietly deleted some of the more provocative passages, and how Diderot did not discover this until right at the end of his labours. The work consequently appeared in a mutilated condition and it is hard to imagine Diderot's feelings. It is indeed surprising to us now that the printer should have felt nervous about these articles, which we can read without alarm. Like Locke's *Essay*, which in spirit they so much resemble, they stand for a point of view which is now commonplace. But at that time the new spirit confronted the old order and supporters of the old order were deeply apprehensive. Only the writings of Voltaire appeared to them more infamous. It has been unfortunate that scientific ideas have had to make their way in the world, not against the resistance of ignorance alone, but against powerful social forces standing for the preservation of the *status quo*. For a very long time scientific speculation was to be mistrusted because of its association with radicalism and scepticism.

The French philosopher Voltaire (1694–1778) is perhaps the most striking of all eighteenth-century literary figures. He makes Dr Johnson look provincial. This is not because of the inherent qualities of his literary productions, most of which are now quite dead in public esteem, but because in his lifetime he happened to bring together in his own interests and activities so many great enthusiasms which we feel are modern and understandable. We can see Voltaire as a champion of justice and education, we can see him diffusing the spirit of liberalism, above all we can hear him pronouncing on the supreme importance of what people believe and on the ultimate victory of true beliefs over those which are false. Rejected and spurned by aristocratic French society young Voltaire (whose real name was François Arouet) spent the years 1726–9 as an exile in England. From these three happy formative years came much that was to be later expressed in his writings. He met Swift, Pope and Gay, he stayed with Bolingbroke and talked interminably with Samuel Clarke who was one of the ablest of Newton's followers. In the course of his long life Voltaire was to become acquainted with a host of personages, including writers, philosophers and mathematicians. His sixteen years' association with the extraordinarily brilliant Marquise du Châtelet appears to have been devoted, at least in part, to a detailed study of the Newtonian system. Voltaire wrote on this system in his *Lettres Philosophiques* and in a work *Philosophie de Newton* which is now to be found only in the collected edition of his works. When he was at the court of Frederick the Great Voltaire got to know Maupertuis, a French mathematician who was chief of Frederick's scientific circle.

How influential Voltaire was in spreading, not a *scientific* account of the Newtonian system, but a more general philosophy in which Newton and Locke represented the modern spirit, it is hard for us to realize, so much better remembered is Voltaire today as a literary or political figure. Indeed Voltaire has no claims to be remembered either as a scientist or mathematician, and he never grappled systematically with the recognized problems of philosophy. But he most acutely contrasted the new work of his age, and especially the work of the English scientists and that of Locke, with the 'babble of antiquity' such as was heard in the teaching of the oldest authorities. For Voltaire the ideas of Newton's *Principia* represented much more than specialized scientific studies. He was indebted here to Clarke for his general understanding of them. But once grasped they were recognized to be something of signal importance to the human race. The *Principia* represented the true approach to the study of phenomena because it brought out the working of natural law. Compared with this Descartes, whom Voltaire did not wholly despise, had provided only a tentative beginning. Vortices were nonsense. Gravity or attraction provided the answer, and it could be shown to do this mathematically. The kind of comment he added can be illustrated in the remark: 'It would be very singular that all nature, all the planets, should obey eternal laws, and that there should be a little animal, five feet high, who in contempt of these laws, could act as he pleased, solely according to his caprice.' In this kind of remark science may be said to spill over into social and moral ideas and there is likelihood of considerable confusion. But Voltaire was not a careful, far less a systematic thinker. He echoes the ideas of Fontenelle but gives them greater human intensity.

Voltaire gave in his *Lettres Philosophiques* (Letters 14 and 15) a most readable account of Descartes compared with Newton, and he did not scruple to refer to their respective characters and circumstances of life in illuminating the great differences to be found in their works. Descartes, he said, might almost have been a poet, for he was a man of brilliant imagination. He quitted France, Voltaire said rather maliciously, because he hoped to find truth, and in France truth was persecuted on account of the miserable scholastic philosophy which prevailed. This was by no means wholly true, and leaves out of account the interesting figures to be found amongst the Paris group of scientists and amateurs at that time. The picture is drawn of a Descartes driven by circumstances and his own nature into a series of adventures which can almost be set beside his own speculative scientific ideas, wandering about Europe and eventually dying under the medical treatment he received from the physician to Queen Christina of Sweden whose teacher he had become. Newton by comparison was fortunate. He was born in a free country and at a time when the follies of scholasticism had become recognized for what they were. Reason alone was cultivated: his countrymen were his pupils not his enemies. This was the gist of Voltaire's comparison.

Where Voltaire relies on his instruction by Samuel Clarke and the book by Henry Pemberton *A View of Sir Isaac Newton's Philosophy*, which he used very freely in Letter 15, he gives his readers rather sounder and less polemical information. Indeed his account of the vortex theory and its inadequacies, and the far superior solutions offered by Newton's 'system of attraction' is both scientifically sound and extremely readable. Voltaire is here to be seen as a great literary figure giving his influence to the scientific movement. But it is to his credit that he gets his science right and teaches his readers an essential lesson which they might not have learned for themselves. This was that the superiority of the Newtonian treatment over the Cartesian lay in its agreement with *measurement*. Not only are the effects in the right direction (which was more than could be claimed for the vortex theory in some circumstances) but they are of the *right order of magnitude*. Pemberton's book was undoubtedly good, but Voltaire was a more stimulating and provocative writer. The points made by Pemberton are delivered in *Lettres Philosophiques* with just a little more point and acerbity.

Nevertheless these letters range quite widely over English life and institutions. There is a lively account of Locke (Letter 13) and 'Chancellor Bacon' (Letter 12). The earliest Letters were on the Quakers, on the Anglican religion, on Parliament, on government, on commerce, while later on he dealt with comedy, tragedy, men of letters, Pope and other famous poets, the Royal Society, and then, having exhausted such themes he devoted a great deal of space to the *Pensées* of Pascal, attacking this writer rather from the point of view of the English deists. The point of view of Deism, as opposed to that of Christianity at that time, was that man is not fundamentally evil and is not in a 'fallen' state. This view, which Voltaire found in certain English writers, agreed very well with his own optimism and belief in the possibility of progress. So that even when Voltaire is discussing the ideas of a fellow countryman it is the English point of view he is concerned to stress.

Voltaire was only one of several Frenchmen who visited England in the early eighteenth century and wrote about their observations. But he was incomparably the most important. Partly, it may well be, out of revenge for the personal humiliations he had experienced in Paris as a young man, but also out of a genuine conviction that the English had stolen an advance on the French, Voltaire expressed in these *Lettres* a biting criticism of much that he disliked in France. Yet his interest in science was genuine even while he puts it forward among other progressive impulses in English civilization. Voltaire was not merely an iconoclastic writer. He laughed at human folly whenever he found it, but he displays beneath his flippancy an earnest belief in the possibilities of European civilization. Much of his life was turbulent with quarrels and disputes. His motto *Ecrasez l'infâme* stood for his hatred of obscurantism and his demand for more 'enlightenment' in human affairs. In *Candide* he laid about him with a deadly wit, but while we are still laughing he produces at the end a pearl of wisdom when he concludes that our duty can be summed up in the words *Il faut cultiver notre jardin:* 'We must cultivate our garden'.

Satirists like Voltaire and Swift undoubtedly saw much that was important in the scientific studies of their time. But they saw much that seemed unimportant or even laughable also. Of the academician whom Gulliver met in Laputa Swift remarked: 'He had been eight years upon a project for extracting sun-beams out of cucumbers, which were to be put into vials hermetically sealed, and let out to warm the air in raw inclement summers'. The King of Brobdingnag by contrast 'gave it for his opinion, that whoever could make two ears of corn, or two blades of grass, to grow upon a spot of ground where only one grew before, would deserve better of mankind, and do more essential service to his country than the whole race of politicians put together'. Swift's attitude is clear. He mocked at science that appeared to him impractical or remote from the immediate circumstances of life. The Laputians, he tells us, never enjoy any peace of mind because of what may happen to the sun, or through the approach of a comet. It was the Laputians who made Gulliver an ill-fitting suit of clothes through making tailoring a branch of mathematics. The Brobdingnagians also employed mathematics but with them this study was 'wholly applied to what may be useful in life, to the improvement of agriculture and all mechanical arts'. This kind of science, practical and unpretentious, received Swift's approval. Voltaire took a larger view. He was all for the moderns against the ancients. He saw science as an emancipating force. Yet Voltaire also disliked scientific pretentiousness. He ridiculed the mathematician Maupertuis, who was employed by the emperor Frederick, for giving himself airs. Perhaps it was only part of Voltaire's attack on Frederick. In a pamphlet he lampooned Maupertuis under the name of Dr. Akkakia. When Maupertuis was engaged in a study of the shape of the earth and the degree to which it is flattened towards the poles Voltaire called him the earth-flattener.

Nevertheless, we can discern in the eighteenth century the

beginnings of a new belief, a belief in progress, that has entered profoundly into the shaping of the modern world. It is significant that Voltaire did not merely admire the science that he found in England. He admired also the rise of a new and free middle class; and a thriving commerce seemed to him to be the basis of a country's prosperity. 'I am not sure, however, which is the more useful to the State,' he wrote, 'a powdered lord who knows precisely at what hour the King rises, and when he goes to bed, and gives himself great airs when he plays the part of slave in the waiting-room of a minister, or a merchant who enriches his country, gives from his office orders to Surat and Cairo, and makes his contribution to the world's well-being.'

This short chapter has been written to correct the impression that the Newtonian synthesis mattered only in science, although from the mid-eighteenth century onwards the withdrawal of science from philosophy became quite marked. Locke's *Essay Concerning the Human Understanding* seems to us to be full of commonplaces, just as Shakespeare's plays are full of quotations, so deeply has his point of view entered into our thinking. Whether he intended it or not, his writing had the effect that science was left free to develop in its own way. Whatever the world-view to which it may give rise there are no limitations to be imposed on it because of prior philosophical considerations. When the Newtonian synthesis was seen to be inadequate it was at first because of scientific reasons. In due course philosophical objections which are serious, if not fatal, to this synthesis were discovered. In modern times it is still believed that no world view based on science can possess more than temporary value. This is unfortunate because the view that science is nothing more than a collection of techniques contributes to a sort of intellectual and moral nihilism such as no society has been able to accept.

For it is not at all an adequate description of science to say that it is a collection of specialized studies, and it is quite untrue to suppose that in the changing condition of scientific knowledge no generally acceptable world view is possible. Far more than education is affected when we see science as somehow in opposition to the arts, and we must indeed despair of the future if we drive the research worker to conclude that he is a mere lackey in a civilization that rests on money, power, and a fashionable and cultivated taste. In the seventeenth century men of science had no need to produce their credentials and establish their right to a share in the culture of their age. It is curious that in the West, in some respects, we have not progressed but have gone backwards here, and a fear of science has arisen which has become linked with an anti-intellectual movement of quite a wide, and professedly philosophical, character. The beginnings of this movement seem to have come from German philosophical writers of the nineteenth century, whose claims, compared with the clarity of a Locke or a Descartes seem preposterous and dangerous, signs, perhaps, that man finds it hard to trust his head and would rather think with his blood, or his bowels, or any other organ than his brain. We may feel deep sympathy with Pascal, who was after all a mathematical genius, when he said that the heart has its reasons which the mind knows nothing of. This is true at one time or another of all of us. But to lose ourselves in that dark flood of Germanic philosophy is another matter. Confronted with writers like Hegel, Schopenhauer, Nietzsche and Fichte we must keep our heads. Existentialism seems today to be in like case—despite the fact that bad philosophy may yet inspire good art.

The values inculcated by science appear not to be universally respected. They include a respect for evidence and a demand for both imagination and disinterestedness. It is very simple. Yet, because it is difficult to resist the desire for certainty in matters where we have little or no evidence, every kind of speculation and ancient superstition are found to persist. We live in a scientific age surrounded with the relics of a medieval past. Even the great seventeenth century has bequeathed to us habits of thought and feeling which are now out of place. Despotic power, and the retention of that privilege which preserves any person or institution from facing the demand for evidence, are things which do not belong to the modern world. And it need scarcely be said that the nationalism of the seventeenth century, and its belief in national sovereignty, both look pretty foolish in our age. It seems incredible that men could know so much and imagine so little. The consequence is that most of our conceptions of political adjustment, and even of personal leadership, belong to a remote period.

CHAPTER SEVEN

Retrospect

THE Newtonian synthesis was the work not of Newton alone but also of some of the best minds of the eighteenth century. By the end of that century it must have seemed a distant age when Charles I 'laughed mightily at Gresham College for weighing air'. Scientific studies of all kinds had gained in prestige and the literary mockers, like Pope and Swift, had less influence. Nevertheless the assumptions of the seventeenth-century thinkers could already be seen to be fallacious. Descartes had concluded that out of matter and mind all the phenomena and all the experiences of the world can be derived. This was a philosophical dualism which has lasted to modern times, and because Descartes presented philosophy with its largest central problem (in these terms) and has thus indirectly been responsible for a considerable literature he has been called the 'father of modern philosophy'. It depends how modern we wish to be. Descartes might well be described as father of all but the most modern developments in philosophy.

Today it is hard for the reader to recapture the belief that the gravitational, inertial, or elastic properties of matter are the ones that provide us with our scientific explanations. This was, however, the belief of men of science in the seventeenth century, Cartesians and followers of Newton alike. For example, heat, once thought to be due to atoms of 'fire', which is a form of Aristotelian teaching, in the seventeenth century was thought of more as an 'intestine commotion of the parts among themselves', in anticipation of the nineteenth-century kinetic theory. Again, since Newton had not dealt with magnetism and electricity in his writings there was a disposition still to follow Descartes's teaching up to the end of the eighteenth century, and to assume that there is a mechanical basis to all such phenomena; the problem was to conceive of the best mechanism which would find its place in Descartes's rational scheme of things. It was when this assumption could no longer be maintained, and for scientific not philosophical reasons, that the fallacy in what we have called the Newtonian synthesis was revealed. Both Descartes and Newton seem to have expected that a unified scientific system of explanations would be established, although Descartes in this respect showed much more confidence, and even impatience, than Newton. None the less Newton's work remains for all time through his emphasis on the mathematical principles rather than the mechanical hypotheses, of which he saw very well there could be many, in science.

What happened in the nineteenth century is well known. The creation of the whole new subject of electro-magnetism was no doubt the greatest single change, amounting to a reversal of the ideas of those who clung too fast to the Newtonian tradition. In this subject we are concerned with the laws according to which electric currents set up magnetic fields, while in the subject of electro-magnetic induction we are concerned with the production of electric currents through changes in the magnetic field in which a conductor is placed. Mechanical conceptions long remained in this field of research, but Clark Maxwell showed they had to be given up. After 1865 it was clear that light also is an electromagnetic, and not a mechanical, type of phenomenon.

The story of the discovery of the nature of light is in fact a very instructive one, and it illustrates very clearly the enormous change in our outlook since medieval times. Then, indeed, light was believed to possess cosmic significance and as it reached the seventeenth century this tradition inclined men to the belief that the phenomena of light best indicated the workings of natural law. It may well be, had we enough detailed information, that an important part of the scientific movement took its rise in this field of study, the other part being concerned principally with mechanics. Indeed there seems to be no doubt that broadly speaking this is true.

Up to the end of the eighteenth century men of science on the whole accepted Newton's theory that light consists of a stream of corpuscles. True, this theory could not account at all well for some quite simple phenomena, which are much better explained on the principles of Huygens's 'wave' theory. But while Huygens's geometrical constructions of the 'wave front' were very elegant there remained the capital difficulty that waves, of whatever kind, tend to spread out, and are not confined to a narrow beam. They also tend to spread round small obstacles placed in their path. It was not until 1803 that Thomas Young demonstrated that in fact these phenomena can be detected, so that the missing evidence for the wave theory existed after all. Then the French physicist Fresnel, with Arago, showed that the vibrations of light cannot be of the sort we have in sound waves, but must be *transverse;* that is, they occur in a plane which is perpendicular to the direction of the light ray. Fresnel was not deterred from accepting transverse waves on the grounds that these cannot be conceived (in a medium which has no surface, or apparently any structure) and in this important respect he represents a new type of scientific thinker. Newton himself would have been at home in the new studies which led up to Clark Maxwell's identification of light as an electro-magnetic disturbance propagated with the same velocity as other electro-magnetic waves. But his restraint concerning all hypotheses was not common and his example proved to be too difficult for the great majority of men of science in the eighteenth and even the nineteenth centuries. All through the nineteenth century scientists tried to imagine the properties of an ether which would transmit electro-magnetic waves and yet which did not oppose any resistance to the motion of the planets. Finally, between the years 1881 and 1887 an important attempt was made to measure the movement of the ether relative to the earth following a suggestion made by Clark Maxwell in 1878.

This 'ether drift' experiment seems today in danger of being forgotten. It was performed first by Michelson working in Germany and later, with more refinements, by Michelson and Morley in America. It was the latter set of experiments that was received by scientists as conclusive. A short account of the work is now given here.

The earth travels in its orbit at about 67,000 miles an hour. It is also spinning. A point on the equator because of spin alone moves through 1,040 miles in one hour. If there is an ether filling all space there should, according to classical ideas, be a reasonable difference in the speed of light according as it travels against the stream of the ether or across the stream. It is not difficult to show that if the velocity of light is c, and the velocity of the ether past the earth at a point on its surface is v, then it takes longer for light to travel a distance x 'up stream' and back than it does to travel the same distance 'across' the stream and back. The ratio of the times should in fact be

$$\frac{1}{\sqrt{1-\frac{v^2}{c^2}}}$$

Now very sensitive means exist for detecting differences of time if we arrange for the waves of light sent out along different paths to be superimposed on each other after they have been reflected back. In these circumstances we can arrange to produce 'interference'. It was to meet the challenge of Clark Maxwell's remarks, in fact, that the famous instrument called the interferometer was invented by Michelson while working in Berlin. 'In the interferometer,' writes a modern authority,[1] 'a beam of light is literally split in two by a "half-silvered mirror", and the two beams of light may be made to travel paths at right angles to each other. At the end of the desired path, each beam is reflected back upon itself and the two come together where they first separated. If the two right-angled paths are optically equal, the reunited beams of light will blend with the waves in concordance. If, however, the paths of the light in the interferometer differ either in actual length or in the optical properties of the medium through which the light passes, differences of phase will result which may be observed as "interference fringes". Observation of these fringes enables one to detect exceedingly small changes in the relative velocities of the light in the two paths of the interferometer, the measurements being made in terms of the wave-length of the light.' This instrument was thought to be quite sensitive enough to detect the expected drift due to the earth's motion. Experiments were carried out in Berlin, and afterwards at Potsdam Observatory. Nevertheless the results obtained were between one-tenth and three-eighths of those expected and it was concluded these were mere experimental errors. There seemed to be no evidence for a stationary ether. It was clear, however, that Michelson was dissatisfied with the work and wished to refine the experiment.

A more thorough investigation was made by Michelson and

[1] D. C. Miller, *Reviews of Modern Physics* (1933).

Morley working in America and the experimental procedure was greatly improved. 'In order to avoid disturbances of vibration and distortion,' writes D. C. Miller, 'the optical parts were mounted on a solid block of sandstone, which was floated on mercury contained in a circular tank of cast iron. This support by flotation made it possible to turn the interferometer to different azimuths while observations were in progress. The practicable limit for the size of the stone base was 150 centimetres square and 30 centimetres thick. In order to obtain the necessary sensitivity, the effective light path was increased by reflecting the light back and forth so that it traversed the diagonal of the square stone block eight times, giving the effect of an interferometer with an arm about 1,100 centimetres in length The expected displacement of the fringes due to a velocity equal to that of the earth in its orbit was 0.4 of a fringe width.'

There is no need to go further into the details of the ether drift experiment. The important point is to grasp the principle of the experiment and to note the results obtained. Michelson and Morley did not obtain a zero effect, but the effect they obtained was between one-twentieth and one-fortieth of the amount expected on theoretical grounds. They concluded that 'the relative velocity of the earth and the ether is probably less than one-sixth of the earth's orbital velocity and certainly less than one-fourth. . . . It appears from all that precedes reasonably certain that if there be any relative motion between the earth and the luminiferous ether, it must be small. . . .'

The sequel to the ether-drift experiment is interesting. The Irish physicist Fitzgerald raised the question how we know, in the Michelson-Morley ether drift experiment, that we can measure two equal distances which are at right angles in relation to the ether drift. If the ether moves in relation to matter might there not be a contraction in the length of a measuring rod held in the direction of the stream, and an expansion when it is held at right angles? On the Continent Lorentz argued that such 'changes' would theoretically be of the right magnitude but could not be detected. All we have to assume is that a length x measured ordinarily must be regarded as a length $x\sqrt{1-\frac{v^2}{c^2}}$ where v is the velocity of the object in the direction in which it is measured with respect to whatever standard of rest we may choose to adopt, and c is the velocity of light. This correction is now regarded as part of the special theory of relativity which arose out of consideration of this sort of problem.

It is now taken for granted that the drift of the ether past the earth cannot be detected, and many would prefer to say there is no such thing as the ether. 'As has often been remarked,' wrote de Broglie in 1932, 'facts serve to produce theories, leading in their turn to the discovery of new facts, which in their turn destroy the theories by which they were discovered.' Since the middle of the nineteenth century the break-up of classical science, and the substitution of revolutionary ideas, has been rapid. The principle of relativity which came into physics in 1905 did a great deal to destroy the hard clear certainty which nineteenth-century science had seemed so surely to be creating. Introduced at first as a principle of restricted range, Einstein's work was later shown to affect several fields of investigation. It was brilliantly expounded in England by A. S. Eddington and there was a dramatic verification of certain theoretical predictions in 1919. The generalized theory came out in Germany in 1915. Owing to the war it was not readily available in this country for another year or two. Eddington's *Space, Time and Gravitation* (1920) presented the public with an up-to-date account and this is still perhaps the best introduction to the subject.

The restricted or special theory of Relativity of 1905 rests on two principles or axioms. The first states that it is impossible to detect uniform motion through the ether. The second states that the velocity of waves travelling away from a source is not affected by the velocity of the source. The conclusions drawn from these two principles come as a matter of formal logic. Einstein showed that absolute space and absolute time, such as were assumed by Newton, are quite unnecessary. They turn out to be 'hypotheses which have nothing to do with any phenomena yet observed and do not afford explanations of any known facts'. All observations are in fact made in respect of a chosen reference frame both with respect to space and time. For reference frames moving uniformly in relation to one another the necessary transformations can be made which enable us to say that the laws are not different for the different reference frames.

It was in the General Theory of 1915 that Einstein extended his work to include accelerated motion between observers and thus brought into existence a new view of gravitation. This part of the theory is more controversial. It is important, therefore, to point to the ways in which Relativity theory is secured by comparison with observation.

According to relativity theory a mass m_0 at low speeds, if given a high velocity v, will increase to a new value m which is given by the formula:

$$m = \frac{m_0}{\sqrt{1 - \frac{v^2}{c^2}}}$$

where c is the velocity of light. (When v becomes equal to c the denominator reduces to zero and the mass m must become infinitely great.) This formula has been verified experimentally in the case of fast-moving electrons and the results are in good agreement with theory.

Historically, however, the most interesting verification of the Einstein theory came from astronomical observations. Here again it has had a complete success. The first example was the explanation of the motion of the planet Mercury. Newton's mechanics demonstrated that the orbit of this planet, like all the rest, should be an ellipse, having the sun at one focus. Using Einstein's mechanics it can be shown that the ellipse of a planet should not exactly close up at the end of one revolution; instead the planet should describe ellipses in slowly changing directions. Mercury has a more elongated ellipse than the other planets and a peculiarity about the orbit had been known for a long time. Indeed an unobserved planet was supposed to be causing perturbations. Perturbations by existing planets do in fact account for a rotation of the ellipse by 532 seconds of a degree per century. The observed rotation was known to be 574 seconds—a discrepancy of 42 seconds. When accordingly, Einstein produced a theoretical calculation which gave a correction of 43 seconds it was clear that this was a striking success for his theory. Later the success was repeated in the case of the planet Mars for which the orbit is much more nearly circular and the effect is much less.

The most dramatic verification of all, however, came in 1919 when eclipse expeditions were sent out by the Royal Society to the Isle of Principe in the Gulf of Guinea and to Sobral in North Brazil. It was fortunate that the war ended in time for these to take place. Not since 1671 had a more important expedition set out to obtain astronomical observations of such general interest. Yet in this case also the results must have seemed sufficiently remote from the affairs of life, for all that was wanted was evidence whether in fact, during the eclipse of the sun, stars seen near the obscured disk are displaced by 2 seconds of a degree from their normal positions in the sky.

The explanation why this displacement was sought is now well known. The Einstein theory predicts the curvature of rays of light passing through a gravitational field. With the planets and the moon the effect is known to be too small to be detectable. It should be detectable when the rays pass near the sun. A difficulty arose in that Newton's mechanics indicate a displacement of the stars also, but only by one-half the amount required by Einstein's theory. Great refinement was needed therefore to decide between the two. Astronomers had in addition to consider whether the passage of light near the sun would be accompanied by ordinary refraction like light passing through our own atmosphere. The evidence against refraction was considered good, however. The required density of gas at some half million miles from the sun's edge would have to be considerable to produce the same effect, and a pressure of some 10,000 atmospheres would be set up on the sun's surface—contrary to spectroscopic evidence. Also the brightness of the stars would be noticeably reduced by such a layer of gas and none of these things was found to take place in practice.

The story of the expeditions has been given in Eddington's *Space, Time and Gravitation,* the frontispiece of which shows the coelostats[1] used by one of the expeditions. The results were, in

[1]When the need is for a large image a telescope of large focal length is used. To avoid the danger that the long tube will bend under its own weight—and to avoid transporting heavy supporting gear—the telescope is mounted horizontally in a fixed position. Light from the sun is directed into the telescope by mirrors one of which is turned by clockwork. This instrument is called a coelostat.

fact, not entirely free from complications, as he explains, but the final figures arrived at carry conviction. Einstein's theory predicted a deflection of 1″.74 at the sun's edge, Newton's 0″.87. The final figures were:

Sobral 1″.98±0″.12
Principe 1″.61±0″.30

the second figures being 'probable accidental errors'.

A new geometricized view of the universe seems to be the broad outcome of the substitution of Einstein for Newton. If his General Theory could be brought to completion natural laws would then all appear as properties of a space-time continuum and all notions of force would vanish. Already the theory has deeply affected our views of the cosmos in which we live. William Herschel proved to be right in thinking that there are galactic systems far outside our own galaxy. We now know that there are millions of galaxies comparable in size with our own. The term 'expanding universe' is used to indicate that in this whole, total, system the galaxies or nebulae are getting further apart.

Quite apart from the new emphasis on the geometry of space-time modern cosmologies represent in another way also a break with the traditional conceptions of Newtonian science.

It is difficult to summarize such a matter because such very different assumptions are used in the various theories at present under consideration. The chief difference between old and new cosmologies seems to be the enormous rate of change now supposed to be going on in the universe. The universe appears to be of vast age, yet it may be that there is no equilibrium in sight. Heinrich Olbers in 1826 remarked that there is much more radiation leaving the stars and nebulae than is absorbed by them. From this starting-point, as H. Bondi has shown in a recent book, *Cosmology* (1952), some interesting conclusions follow. In general the new theoretical schemes have to apply not to vast systems in conditions of equilibrium but to systems in a state of most violent disturbance. This characteristic of violence appears clearly in theoretical work on the structure of stars and on possible ways in which our solar system may have been formed. The transformation of mass into energy plays an important part in cosmic change; without this conception we should still be in the dark about the sources of stellar energy. Unfortunately it is impossible to do justice to modern work within the limits of a short and non-technical review. There is the further difficulty that ideas change rapidly and any selection that is made can easily be criticized because the work referred to has been superseded.

It had become clear in the nineteenth century that the sun could not maintain its production of energy by ordinary chemical changes. This followed immediately when sufficiently accurate estimates of the rate of radiation had been obtained. During the first half of the century the results obtained in calculations of the amount of heat reaching the earth (in a given latitude) were all vitiated through uncertainty about the amount of atmospheric absorption. The American astronomer Langley, working at Alleghany, was responsible for the most important work on the rate of solar radiation. His method was to make observations of the energy distributed throughout the sun's spectrum by means of the spectrometer and an instrument called the bolometer which he invented for this purpose. The radiation of any given wave-length band is absorbed in this instrument by a fine strip of platinum foil covered with lamp black, and a delicate electrical method shows the rise of temperature produced in the foil. By making simultaneous 'spectro-bolometric' observations at the summit of Mount Whitney in the Californian Sierra Nevada, and at the foot of the mountain 11,000 ft. below, Langley was able to determine the atmospheric absorption as it affected various wave-lengths. From the observed distribution of energy in the sun's spectrum it was possible to construct a graph which gave clearly the wave-lengths between which the maximum intensity of radiation lay. Experimental work by Stefan (1879) and theoretical work by Boltzmann and by Wien provided means of arriving at the temperature of the sun's outer layers. Meanwhile other physical methods were contributing more information on which later theories had to rest. The spectra of many thousands of stars showed that they were in a gaseous condition and measurements of the diameters of some of the largest stars revealed some truly astonishing magnitudes. The interferometer invented by Michelson, for example, used on the star Betelgeuse showed that its diameter must be of the order of 250 million miles—nearly the diameter of the orbit of the planet Mars.

H. N. Russell of Princeton contributed some of the most important work on the theory of stellar evolution. All such work is highly technical but the results can be simply described. A star is thought to begin its life history as a large diffuse and relatively cool sphere of gas. Contraction under gravity reduces its surface and raises its temperature so that its spectrum changes steadily even while its apparent brightness may show little change—the decrease in area and increase in brilliance counteracting each other as regards apparent brightness. The contraction ceases, according to theory, when the interior ceases to behave as a perfect gas. After this the maximum temperature is passed and cooling begins. Shrinkage of the surface now continues with fall of temperature so that there is a decrease in brightness, and in the end the star is again red and finally dies out of sight altogether. An important distinction between 'giant' and 'dwarf' stars, made by Hertzsprung, was introduced also by Russell, and the classification he has evolved has become firmly established even while difficulties remain in the theory of stellar development. There seems to be sufficient evidence for the conclusion that stars begin as masses of vapour flung into space from the arms of spiral nebulae and that they are of approximately the same size to begin with. Jeans's *Astronomy and Cosmogony* contains some interesting studies of the dynamics of gaseous and liquid masses in a state of rotation and some of his conclusions may be of permanent value. Jeans believed that we should replace the notion of a gradual shrinkage of stars by the notion of contraction by spasms, a star remaining of about the same size through a long period of time, after which a fairly rapid contraction occurs. 'This jerkiness of contraction is ultimately due to the fact that the atoms out of which stars are built are not continuous structures. . . . As the temperature changes, the size of the atom necessarily changes by a whole ring [of electrons] at a time, and these jumps in the sizes of the atoms shew themselves in jumps in the sizes of the stars.' On the dynamical side it makes a great difference to the result of rotation if the mass is gaseous rather than liquid. It seems to follow from Eddington's arguments that this is very often the case. Eddington called attention to the enormous pressures which must be set up under the force of gravity in the central parts of stars. Very high temperatures, running into millions of degrees Centigrade, are inferred for this part of a star and at these temperatures the maximum energy must be associated with very short wave-length radiation of the type of X-rays. The energy of these rays is enough to remove layers of electrons so that the atoms are very small and highly charged. Under these conditions the interior of a star, in spite of the high pressures, behaves like a perfect gas. We therefore have the paradoxical result that while the density of matter in the interior may be extremely high—hundreds of times that of lead, the material has the properties of a gas. Inside a star there is a 'hurly-burly of atoms, electrons, and ether waves. Dishevelled atoms tear along at 100 miles a second, their normal array of electrons being torn from them in the scrimmage. . . .'

With the conception that stars are gaseous in constitution it was natural to inquire whether the loss of stellar matter could be regarded as the source of the planetary system surrounding our sun. In 1917 Jeans and Jeffreys made the suggestion that the close passage of another star might have caused a long filament of incandescent matter to be drawn out of the sun by gravitational action and this filament could then condense and cool to produce planets. The difficulty in the theory, as Nolke in Germany and Russell at Princeton pointed out in 1930, is that this process could not allow for the observed angular momentum observed in the solar system; a grazing collision could not start the filament of planetary material off with anything like enough angular momentum. This difficulty started astronomers on a hunt for new ideas. Hoyle showed that if one of two close stars blew up, as novae are known to do, the explosion might occur in such a way that a little of the stellar material remained in the vicinity of the other star and so gave rise to satellites. According to Spitzer the chief difficulty of any theory depending on the use of material from the interior of a star is that it would not under any ordinary circumstances condense into planets but would expand with explosive force to form a gaseous nebula. For this reason some astronomers have gone back to the old idea that the planets are derived from nebulous matter and a theory on these lines has been proposed by the German physicist Weizsacker. Weizsacker starts with a large cloud of dust and gas in rotation about a massive central body like the sun. He concludes that while most of the gas would escape into outer space, the planets could be formed by the condensation of the dust particles over a period of some 100 million years—a short time compared with the age of the earth. According to Spitzer's theory, which was once popular, stars themselves may be formed from interstellar matter under the pressure of radiation received from other stars in some cases, and Bok, who has propounded similar arguments, believes that certain astronomical objects in the Milky Way may represent stars which are being formed in this manner. In this case the solar system may have been formed at the same time as the sun. Against this the arguments of Hoyle, based on a consideration of the known chemical constitution of the stars and such bodies as the earth, may have some force. If his ideas about the atomic processes occurring during the flare-up of a super-nova are substantially correct they would go far to explain the high proportion of heavy elements in the earth's crust. About the earth's interior, however, we have really quite insufficient knowledge. It is clear that this particular problem of scientific cosmogony is still in a very obscure condition. As Page of the Yerkes Observatory has recently remarked, there exists today 'no real theory of the origin of the earth in the sense of a complete logical structure linking together the vast quantity of pertinent observations collected during the last century'.

The story of modern science could be continued at very great length and much of it would illustrate the great change in our explanations, and the uncertainties that surround us on all sides. There is, however, a general philosophical point to be brought out at the end of this book without which we shall not be clear what it was that was peculiarly characteristic of Newtonian science. For in an important sense Newtonian science is now dead and can be contemplated as can any other important episode in the history of thought. We can hope to understand it as we cannot hope to understand contemporary developments in physics.

At the core of Newtonian science is the aim to discover what is permanent, what is 'conserved', during many of the changes that we observe going on around us. It would be idle to maintain that Newton's science embraced them all, for of course it did not. Newton followed the clues that had been discovered before him and concentrated his attention on those phenomena which yielded to a mathematical approach. Nothing has been said about his experimental work in chemistry because it was not successful. And biology, which has quite an interesting history in the seventeenth century, has been totally excluded from this little survey for the same reason. Newtonian science seemed to show that quantities like mass, velocity, acceleration, and later on kinetic energy and mechanical work, provided a set of fundamental explanatory principles. With the rise of chemistry it seemed quite certain for a long time that the *masses* of atoms must be their most important characteristic. It was all part of the collapse of this scheme when it was shown that atomic mass is not of such special significance, and that the electric charge on the nucleus of an atom is more important.

When it was found that atoms can disintegrate, as happens in radioactivity, it was understandable that scientists should suppose that the subatomic particles, such as electrons and protons, retained the permanence that had been reserved for atoms. Some things, it was felt, *must* be indestructible. Why this belief was so strong it is hard to say. It has a long history and seems to arise out of a fundamental desire to understand things in a particular way. The Newtonian scheme postulated a framework of time and space within which certain transformations constantly go on. The medieval conception of a region of changelessness and perfection was quite abolished, it is true, but in its place men inherited an equally uncertain set of principles which prevailed all the more powerfully because they seemed to rest on observation and experiment. We may well doubt if the great mass of mankind can rid themselves of these prejudices, for very probably ordinary thought will continue to be Newtonian long after complete changes have occurred in scientific thinking. We can already see that mass and energy together are now popularly supposed to represent some kind of combination of ideas that stand for permanence or conservation. Yet energy is a totally different notion from that of mass and we delude ourselves if we think we have preserved our old beliefs by clinging on to this newer conception just as the Newtonians clung to mass. Very probably we have to do without the belief that we can identify what is permanent behind the flux of events. In olden times men used to say 'God has made a universe that we can understand.' Today we can say 'In human experience there are phenomena which we can reduce to order in a mathematical way.'

We are surrounded by mystery. Time and again it has seemed as if a more or less complete comprehension of certain groups of natural phenomena have been achieved, but invariably this belief has proved false. Only a hundred years ago the atom was thought of as a tiny particle surrounded by a field of force which might be of electrical and was almost certainly not of gravitational nature. Along the lines of the classical atomic theory it seemed as if a satisfactory account could be confidently expected and that it was unlikely that any radical change would occur in the scientific outlook. Today we have the new and vast subject of atomic physics and there can be few indeed who expect to see this subject tidied up or brought to completion in another fifty years. The history of science gives no encouragement to such an idea.

On the other hand there is no certainty that the search for valid relationships will be and must be endless. We just do not know. We do not know how much importance to attach to that conviction that many distinguished scientists share that the system of relationships established in physics must be unified and not fall into disconnected divisions. We know that Einstein was convinced that gravitational and electro-magnetic effects must be connected in theory, but it is not certain up to the present that the relationship will be found, or that it necessarily exists. It may be that we have to accept such a dichotomy as irremovable. We treat light sometimes as if it were a wave-process, sometimes as a stream of photons. Electrons, protons, and even atoms also have certain wave-properties.

It is a long time since the 'picturable' quality of scientific explanations was felt to matter very much. In the nineteenth century Kelvin believed he could only progress in a piece of work if he could make a model or otherwise imagine the mechanics of the phenomenon. Since his time we have learned that the quantities we find it difficult or impossible to picture to ourselves are best left as mathematical quantities, defined by mathematical equations and manipulated mathematically. All other definitions of such quantities (as for example of entropy or potential) are sure to be found extremely unsatisfactory. The belief that physics is concerned with the construction of a conceptual world is found in the works of many writers on the subject. This reminds us of the Platonic philosophy. It seems incongruous when we reflect how long ago, and how drastically, Platonism was extirpated from science, but we should be accustomed by this time to the sight of philosophy creeping in whenever a developed science exists. The fact is that it is exceedingly difficult, and perhaps undesirable, to keep 'philosophy' out if by this word we simply mean the propensity of the human mind to seek a connected view of things and not to be satisfied with a multiplicity of separate principles.

There have been two main points of view about the nature of the explanations given by physics, such for example as the nature of the electron 'discovered' in 1897. According to the 'realists' the electron really exists and is described by all the equations we happen to be able to give concerning its 'behaviour'. According to the 'positivists' the electron is not an entity at all and we cannot therefore discuss its 'existence'. It is a name given to a mental concept which enables us to clarify our thinking about phenomena. Eddington in *The Nature of the Physical World* and other books, all very stimulating to read, gave support to this point of view, but Planck and Einstein opposed this and believed that science became reduced to an absurdity, and that logically progress became impossible, unless we accept the realist standpoint. The sad fact seems to be that we have no simple means of deciding whether physics reveals more and more of the true nature of things, or whether as the positivists imply, the human mind is caught up in an explanatory network of its own creation. Certain developments in modern philosophy appear to deflate the importance of some of these disputes and the tendency is to pay less and less attention to them.

Nevertheless the influence of science on thought has continued to increase since Newton's time and it seems desirable to see, if we can, in what direction this has occurred. What in Chapter Six was described as the mainly psychological effects of technology should not be underestimated. These effects are widespread and powerful. They have been considered in Lewis Mumford's book *Science and Technics,* and the fact that this book was written with the American civilization in mind now matters less than it did. But the most profound effects of science are unquestionably in the imaginative outlook of people who have been educated in science, and as the number of such people must increase steeply in the future so these influences, or characteristics of the scientific as opposed to the literary, historical, or humanistic type of mentality are sure to increase. We can see quite clearly, when we look back to Voltaire, or even to Locke, that such influences have been at work continuously, and they are of such a nature that the change from Newtonian to modern physics probably makes little difference. For nothing in modern physics contradicts the importance of natural law and the sort of ethical neutrality and intellectual disinterestedness which the existence of natural law in the world appears strongly to engender in the human mind.

So long as any trace of ancient explanations remained the human mind could not escape the suspicion that the events of Nature, and still more the events of the individual human life, reflected a *moral* governance of the world. The importance of the Good in Plato's philosophy is well known. The withdrawal from Platonism that broadly characterizes the change over to scientific explanations has profound implications for modern life. Indeed they are so profound and disturbing that most people who wish to see the preservation of the *status quo* in human conduct and belief prefer to talk as if these implications did not exist. Science, it can be argued, does not provide us with a basis of morals and therefore our traditional beliefs and standards might as well be accepted; which is much the position adopted by John Locke.

Now it is one thing to say that science does not provide a basis of morals or a whole philosophy of life; it is quite another thing to say that the system of morals or the general philosophy adopted should be consistent with a scientific outlook and with a view of the world that takes our science into account. This seems, broadly, to be the problem that people educated through science are finding more and more important and it is a problem that more and more receives the attention of individual men who find themselves obliged to approach the matter independently.

In his famous Romanes lecture of 1893 Thomas Henry Huxley grappled with the fact that the process of evolution established by Darwin was clearly devoid of moral considerations. But this absence of moral considerations in the living world was merely what students of cosmology since Newton had taken for granted. It was more painful to confront it in the world of living organisms but it could not be regarded as unexpected. In the whole world, so our science seems to show, there are events which occur in accordance with certain natural laws. There is nothing to be gained by asking what good (or evil) is served by these events and to this extent we find ourselves adopting the point of view of the philosopher Spinoza. But of course the gain in human emancipation is very great, and it seems certain that only through the inculcation of a new degree of detachment of mind can more of our problems be brought within the range of scientific understanding. However displeasing events may be, however personally they may affect us, it is imperative that we should not lose sight of them as events which have been brought about by particular circumstances which we must try to see in the light of scientific law.

Perhaps the simplest way of describing this change that has been brought about by the scientific movement is to say that an ancient notion of Providence has today vanished from our thinking. For it is clear that men have always regarded as the workings of Providence those events that brought the fulfilment of their desires while other events which tended in other directions were ignored. 'Where are the votive tablets of those who perished in spite of their vows?' Bacon asked on a famous occasion. And he was voicing in advance a general change that was to take place, condemning all forms of superstition, compelling men to recognize, even though they might not become easily reconciled to, the force of natural law.

To attach a longer appendage to a small book on Newtonian science would not be justifiable. The scientific movement of the past three hundred years involves more than physics and its full character cannot be shortly summed up in a page or two. But

Newtonianism, it has been stressed, has been the beginning of the modern world. While Newtonian physics is now dead the stimulus it gave to thought continues to be immense. The decline of Platonism ever since the times of the nominalist-realist conflict, the victory of empiricism and the defeat of the doctrine of innate ideas, the discarding even from Newton's scheme of all elements that are not justified represents the dismantling of a great façade with which learning has so long impressed the world. What lies behind the façade seems untidy, inchoate and uncertain. On the basis of twentieth-century science we can make fewer claims than could Laplace in the eighteenth century. And yet the general import of science has not decreased, but has greatly increased, in the intervening period. It is characteristic of our situation that we make no dogmatic claims. We have to live without dogma.

A SHORT BIBLIOGRAPHY

E. N. da C. Andrade *A Brief History of the Royal Society* (1960)
Sir Isaac Newton (1954)

A. Armitage *Copernicus* (1938)

A. E. Bell *Christian Huygens and the Development of Science in the Seventeenth Century* (1947)

E. T. Bell *Men of Mathematics* (1937)

W. W. Bryant *Kepler* (1920)

E. Burtt *The Metaphysical Foundations of Modern Science* (1932)

H. Butterfield *The Origins of Modern Science 1300–1800* (1949)

Sir George Clark *The Seventeenth Century* (2nd Edn. 1947)

A. C. Crombie *Augustine to Galileo* (1952)

Descartes *A Discourse on Method* (Everyman edition)

H. Dingle *Science and Human Experience* (1931)

J. L. E. Dreyer *History of Planetary Theories from Thales to Kepler* (1906)

Réne Dugas *Mechanics in the Seventeenth Century* (1958)

P. Duhem *L'Evolution des Théories Physiques* (1896)

Sir A. S. Eddington *Space, Time and Gravitation* (1920)
The Nature of the Physical World (1928)

J. J. Fahie *Galileo* (1929)

H. A. L. Fisher *A History of Europe* (1936)

Galileo Galilei *Dialogues Concerning the Two Chief Systems of the World* (trans. Salusbury 1661)
Dialogues Concerning Two New Sciences (trans. Crew and de Salvio 1914). *Reprinted:* Dover Publications (Constable)

A. B. Gibson *The Philosophy of Descartes* (1932)

Sir Harold Hartley (Editor) *The Royal Society, its Origins and Founders* (1960)

P. Hazard *The European Mind* (1953)

R. F. Jones (and others) *The Seventeenth Century* (Stanford, 1951)

H. B. W. Joseph *Lectures of the Philosophy of Leibnitz* (1949)

Kepler *Tercentary Commemoration Papers* (1931)

L. T. More	*Isaac Newton* (1927)
Isaac Newton	*Optics* (reprint of the 4th edition 1931)
	Principia trans. Motte, 1848 (and reprinted under editorship of F. Cajori 1934)
F. L. Nussbaum	*The Triumph of Science and Reason 1660–85* (1953)
David Ogg	*Europe in the Seventeenth Century* (5th Edn. 1960)
De L. O'Leary	*How Greek Science Passed to the Arabs* (1949)
Max Planck	*Where is Science Going?* (1933)
	A Scientific Biography and Other Papers (1950)
W. D. Ross	*Aristotle* (1930)
P. Rousseau	*Histoire de la Science* (1945)
Charles Singer	*Short History of Science* (1941)
Charles Singer and C. Rabin	*Prelude to Modern Science* (1946)
D. E. Smith	*History of Mathematics* (1923–5)
A. J. Snow	*Matter and Gravity in Newton's Physical Philosophy* (1926)
J. W. N. Sullivan	*The Bases of Modern Science* (1928)
J. W. Thompson	*History of the Middle Ages* (1931)
E. L. Thorndike	*History of Magic and Experimental Science* (1923–41)
Stephen Toulmin	*The Philosophy of Science* (1953)
C. E. Vulliamy	*Voltaire* (1930)
A. N. Whitehead	*Science and the Modern World* (1937)
B. Willey	*Seventeenth Century Background* (1934)
	Eighteenth Century Background (1940)

This book was printed before I had discovered the new work by Réne Dugas (Editions du Griffon, Switzerland) or the writings of R. F. Jones of Stanford University which have only in recent years appeared in books which are readily available in England. R. F. Jones's writings are of great interest for an understanding of a topic which has scarcely been considered here: the relations between the men of science on the one hand, and on the other, the religious thinkers and literary men of the seventeenth and eighteenth centuries.

A.E.B.

INDEX